Ronald McKie is a Queenslander who now lives in Melbourne. For forty years he was a journalist in Brisbane then Melbourne and Asia. During the Second World War he served as a private in the AIF before becoming a war correspondent for the *Sunday Daily Telegraph* and the *London Evening Standard*. He has published three novels, *The Mango Tree, The Crushing* and *Bitter Bread*. His non-fiction work includes Second World War documentaries: *Proud Echo* and *The Heroes*, political and social studies of Southeast Asia, and *We have No Dreaming* – a personal walkabout through the eighty-one years of Ronald McKie's life. He is married with one son and two granddaughters.

Also by Ronald McKie
and available in Imprint

We Have No Dreaming

IMPRINT

THE MANGO TREE

RONALD McKIE

Collins
Publishers
Australia

For Anne

COLLINS PUBLISHERS AUSTRALIA
First published in 1974 by William Collins Pty Ltd.
55 Clarence Street, Sydney NSW 2000
This edition published in 1989

Copyright © Ronald McKie 1974

National Library of Australia
Cataloguing-in-Publication data:

McKie, Ronald, 1909-
The Mango Tree.
ISBN 0 7322 2529 9.
I. Title.
A823'.3

Printed by Globe Press, Victoria
Cover Photograph courtesy John Oxley Library

CHAPTER ONE

A BLACK WIND from across the mountains brought dust and grass seeds and a melancholy crying. It cuffed the long leaves of the mango tree, threw powdered cane trash against the windows. It spread dark stains on the river and the stains travelled with the tides until they were absorbed or taken to sea.

After three days the wind stopped and into the silence came another, sticky with salt and stinking of weed, but cool and soft from the southern marches of the Coral Sea, so that in the piccaninny daylight of that Christmas Eve, as the men left the scrub that clamped the town against the river and came down the long street, their flannels stained a darker grey, their boots fresh-blacked with dew, the morning was still and cloudless and splashed with birds.

Some of the drivers sat their carts and drays, legs free beside the shafts, while others walked against their sweating horses or beside their whispering loads. And one, a tall youth with copper hair and a face too long and old for his body, carried his axe across his shoulder.

Then the men began to sing, and the crude voices fell against the buildings and argued over the river, so that even the magpies stopped their squabbling and the swallows, peering from their brown mud nests on the Water Tower, took fright and wing. The men sang, as they had in earlier days when the bullock teams arrived from the south over tracks cut by waggon wheels. And from that time, when the town was a mining camp, singing had become a ritual, a memory of deliverance and rejoicing, on Christmas Eve.

Now the town stirred in its sleep, until windows squealed and faces were framed in opening doorways as the men came nearer. The dogs emerged first to howl and mill and frighten the horses. The children followed, in nightdresses and striped pyjamas, tangled hair and pigtails, and with the dogs they shrilled beside the wheels that kicked a muslin dust into the still air. Parents followed, flannelette gowns over night clothes and one or two of the very old in night caps, to wave and call, though most stayed within the modesty of half-opened windows and verandah shutters on which the dust lay like brown paste.

Then the sun, climbing at last above the high crater of the Mount that Cook had seen and Flinders had charted, fired the scarlet tips of the swaying loads, polished the marching faces, flickered on silver buckles, on revolving hubs, on the brasses swaying like orders from the damp collars of the horses.

When the drays reached the old water trough, hollowed from an ironbark log, where the shops began, the singing stopped, as abruptly as it had begun. There the shopkeepers and their helpers waited. The grocers in white shirts with rolled sleeves, held up with rubber armlets, and long white aprons clamped at the back with long pins tipped with brass hearts and anchors and stars; the butchers in their tartan woollen aprons and blue and white striped shirts with cut-off sleeves; the drapers in black suits and high collars, their coats off and starched cuffs turned back from their wrists. Even the barber, his whalebone comb, without which he would have felt undressed, above his right ear, and the undertaker, since business was slack this Christmas Eve, were there to decorate the town, part of the custom that traced back sixty years to when the gold petered out and the first German settlement was built and the first sugar planted.

2

As some of the draymen unloaded, others piled the fresh-cut gum-branches in damp heaps along the street where the shopkeepers, mindful of the traditional division of labour on this day, carried them to the footpaths. There they sorted and tied them, with yellow hemp twine, to the posts that supported the curving roofs protecting their customers and their windows from the sun. Soon the covered ways on either side of Boola Street were leafy tunnels and the antiseptic smell of bruised leaves and torn bark drifted into the shops and homes to cool and cleanse the town.

Only when the street was dressed in its Christmas greenery, as far down as the shops of Chinatown, and the men had stabled their horses, did the owners of the Royal and the Commercial, and the seedy Imperial where the canecutters from the south packed five to a room in the season, set a combined keg on a trestle in the centre of the street and serve free, but only to those who had cut and carried and tied, a glass of rum with a beer chaser as a breakfast of thanksgiving.

Magpies were squabbling with a butcher-bird in the silky oaks along River Street when Jamie went home. He cleaned his axe, brushing the edge with the stone as Scanlon had taught him, and propped it in a corner of the toolshed. Then he entered the sprawling white house, with its tall chimneys and verandahs on three sides, in gardens that lost themselves in the river.

As he showered and changed his clothes he could tell by the muted sounds – the far slam of the pan on the black range, the oven door kicked shut as the hot plates were taken out – that breakfast was almost ready. He gave a last stab to his hair with the military brushes his grandmother had given him on his last birthday and went along the dim hall to the dining room.

She was already seated. He kissed her on her witch's head.

'The Huns have a gun that'll throw a shell thirty miles. Jackie Winn saw it in the paper.'

'So I read.' Dry as quinces. 'But I won't have war at the breakfast table.'

She looked over her spectacles. 'You didn't touch that gut rot?'

He shook his head. 'It stinks.'

'Good. You can have a glass of ale – only one mind you – before those heathens arrive.'

'Oh, Gran . . . I'll be seventeen next year.'

'That's what concerns me. Mother, bless her departed soul, called it the devil's year.'

He questioned with his eyes.

'The year of temptation.'

He grinned. 'You sound just like Preacher Jones. I bet you did some tempting when you were a girl.'

'I daresay,' she said. 'At least I knew what the shearers had in mind.'

They were laughing as Pearl brought in the food.

The shops opened an hour earlier that one day of the year, and already the farmers were moving into town. From down river where the mangroves grew thirty feet above the mud, from upstream beyond the second rapids where the cattle hills began, from near Black Scrub where the flying foxes camped in millions, from farms along a coast of golden bays and tumbled basalt where the breadfruit trees were spiders on the headlands. And from further out, Tara and Emu Creek and Nut Hill where the tribes had gathered under truce not so long ago when the trees were bearing to share, in suspended enmity, nature's gifts. And further still. From the muttering tea-tree swamps beyond Saxony where the black and white swans and green duck and black duck and teal anchored at dusk among a mulch of frogs and rotting bark and weed, and

4

the bronzewings and cockatoos and white Torres pigeons, on their annual migration from New Guinea, made Chinese ideographs among the trees.

The heavy waggons, inherited from southern Germany, came in early. Their horseteams wore white sunhats, held on by their ears which fitted through slits in the stiff canvas. The hats, which were decorated for Christmas by the children with nasturtiums and mignonette and purple bougainvillea, gave the horses demure expressions. Jamie thought they looked like shy girls at their first party.

The squat springless waggons, some blue, some red with flowers painted on them, had splayed sides and high wheels with spokes – thicker than a man's arm – that churned the dust and shimmering air of summer, and under the tailboards ran the dogs, their tongues long pink straps almost touching the ground.

The waggons carried the scrubbed and starched farmers and their families, the men stifling in black off-the-peg suits and broad hats and greased boots, the women in long muslins and wide straws, the little girls with shining faces and pigtails yellow as the sea-snakes that bred in the rock pools along the coast.

The rains had come early and would return. The cutting and crushing was finished. The dust, brick red in some areas, chocolate in others, and as white and fine as flour in the Hungry Country to the south, stained the air over all the roads and tracks leading into town.

The farmers came mostly in the big waggons, but others were in drays and spring carts and duckboards and glistening sulkies sporting high whips and polished lamps and oiled harness. They came on horseback wearing green saddle-twist trousers, white shirts and stained hats, on Indian motor cycles, on push bikes and even on foot. And through the un-natural crush, since on weekdays one could travel for miles in any direction without meeting a soul, came a rare Delage or a Talbot, their drivers in motoring coats, caps and goggles and wearing long gauntlets, their women passengers in dust coats and veils tied over their hats and under their chins, and all proudly superior as they passed the horse vehicles.

By noon, when the town band, sweating in blue serge and gold braid, their Guards caps bearing big brass harps, marched up Boola Street to the Royal and began to play the *Blue Danube* on the first floor verandah, the farmers brought their Christmas presents to the big house on River Street. As they always had when Jamie's father was alive.

The Germans came first, and never a minute before or after twelve. Descendants, most of them, of emigrants from the political troubles of the eighteen forties, they still spoke the dialects of homeland principalities, still taught them to their children, still worshipped in the bleak Lutheran chapels of their grandparents' youth. Yet they were fiercely Australian, too fiercely some, at a time when their ancestral homeland was at war and 'Hun' or 'Boche' worse than an insult. They suffered the hurt and nostalgia all immigrants feel who are torn between the traction of new life and old blood, of ancient ways and harsh beginnings. And the hurt was compounded when, early in the war and at Kitchener's call, some of the young men had volunteered and had been rejected because of their origins. During those years of war, many kept to themselves on their farms and avoided the town as much as possible, except at Christmas and Easter. The drunken insult, though rare, happened.

They were, many of them, tall heavy men with creased necks from too much sun and fair moustaches waxed at the ends to pencil points. They smelt of Monkey Soap and starch and camphor. Their white shirts glistened. And some were tieless, their shirt-necks closed with brass studs.

They brought food, for what else would descendants of fine

6

peasants bring in return for help and favours. They pulled off their broad hats and bowed to Grandmother. They gripped her hand so hard and pumped it so vigorously that after they had left she wrung the pain and said, 'They're good people – drat them.'

They laid their Christmas presents on the verandah which stank of garlic, so she complained, for weeks. Dark-smoked hams from pigs fed only on milk, vegetables, fruit and corn, and first soaked in brine, alum, cloves and raw sugar; sides of bacon, pink and delicious; necklaces of brown sausages, exploding with garlic; blood puddings packed with spices; young corn cobs with dew still sparkling on their pale green shirts; bags of peaches, nurtured on pig manure, that squirted a sugary juice; baskets of strawberries and billies of yellow cream; ripening persimmons, guavas, granadillas, and only their finest dolphin mangoes, as big as a six months old baby's head, that had no strings and could be custard spooned.

The Chinese waited until the German farmers had finished their second glass of ale and had left to rejoin their families. The German women never appeared. The Germans ignored the Chinese and seldom patronised their shops. No meeting ground, no common empathy, existed between the two races. To the Germans, and to most older Australians, they were Chinamen or Chinee or Chinks or Chows and inferior. Even townspeople who did business with them and liked them, did not mix. Chinatown was a ghetto, physically and in most minds.

Jamie's grandmother, who owned property in the district, was one of the rare few who knew the homes behind their shops and was welcome there, as she was in the farmhouses of the Germans, and her son, before he was killed in the train crash at Sara Creek, and her grandson, had been reared with none of the prejudices of others in the town. Jamie liked the Germans, though they were too serious and seldom smiled, but he preferred the Chinese, except when he was very young.

The Chinamen did not stamp up the steps and stand ramrod stiff as the Germans did. They emerged among their offerings, as though they had materialised from the air. Small serious men, all Cantonese, who bowed deeply to Grandmother in her long white dress and whalebone collar and thin heavily padded iron-grey hair, greeting her in a mixture of their own dialect, which she partly understood, and broken English.

When Jamie was small, he had faced this annual Christmas ceremony with feelings close to terror. The Chinese gave him spiders and a dry mouth, especially Ling Shing Shu who became excited when his English was not understood and danced from foot to foot and clasped his ears in semantic exasperation. His right eye, too, since his blind left eye was covered in scars from an old injury in Canton that he would never discuss, glittered so demonically that for years Jamie believed that Ling was only waiting his chance to slit him from earhole to earhole after unspeakable torture. But now the Chinese, even old Ling, were friends and he had almost forgotten the Christmas Eves when he had peeped from behind his grandmother's skirts at the alarming yellow men with slit eyes who smelt strongly of very old fruit.

The Chinese brought their presents in wickerwork baskets or wrapped in thin bamboo mats or in scarlet paper. A moment Jamie had always loved, even when he was very young and terrified. For Pearl, but mainly for Grandmother, so much each year that she sent some of the gifts to friends and relatives in the south. She gave away nothing locally. She had no wish to hurt the feelings of her Chinese friends.

Bolts of white and cream silk, handwoven and so fine that Jamie shuddered with delight at the softness of the cloth; hand-painted silk fans; sandalwood handkerchief boxes, deeply carved and smelling of perfumed heaven when he sank his nose in them; green and grey urns of ginger in thick syrup and shallow boxes lined with crinkly tin that contained dry sugared ginger so hot that one piece paralysed the tip of his tongue; scented tea in tins and red packets painted with junks and waterfalls and Manchu princesses and screaming with black and gold characters; baskets of dried lichees, their skins like grandmother's neck, sweet-sour and so aromatic that they gave Jamie a belly ache if he ate too many of them, but whose perfume made him aware, as he grew, of the smell of girls; watermelons so ripe they crackled inside like brown paper when he knelt on them and so sugary that the red pulp melted in his mouth as mysteriously as the snows he had never seen, except in picture books at the School of Arts. And for Jamie, fish and dragon paper kites that floated so gracefully in the lightest air, paper lanterns and temples to hang from a nail, puzzles of wood and wire, carvings of horses and buffaloes and tigers and even cicadas, boxes and boxes of Bungers, Basket Bombs, Jumping Jacks, Tom Thumbs, Roman Candles, Sparklers, Throwdowns, Flower Pots, Falling Rain and Rockets of all sizes that exploded on Guy Fawkes Night above the river in echoing thunder and slow falling stars.

The Chinese would not touch beer or spirits so Pearl made China tea which all drank from small bowls with much sipping and sucking that Jamie knew was polite before Ling Shing Shu, his good eye smiling, led him to the backyard and hung yards of Tom Thumbs Chinese fashion on a clothesline and set them off in rattling explosions that scared every devil, so he said, for hundreds of yards and might even give Peter Ma Chu, the cook at the Royal, who was a foolish fellow and a republican who no longer believed in evil spirits, something to think about.

In the long afternoon, when the bandsmen had blown themselves bloodshot and had at last stacked their instruments

9

on the Royal verandah, the young children slept with the dogs under the waggons and sulkies along the river bank and the older children played until they dropped on fire in their sweaty clothes to lie and stare at the clouds drifting in like galleons from the sea. Now the women, too full of food to move, their household chatter spent, loosened their stays and kicked off their boots and shoes and lay in the black shade of the Moreton Bay figs that had been there long before the town had been a gold camp. While they rested, the men packed the bars and washed down rum with beer and forgot their troubles and laughed and spewed and sometimes fought until they were pulled apart and made see reason with a pot of beer over their heads and another down their collars.

As the fig-tree shadows lengthened and the heat ebbed, the children woke, their mothers stirred, stretched and reached for their shoes. The older boys took the chaff-bags off the horses and led them, snuffling and tossing, to the waggons and began to harness up. And as the last cask emptied, the reluctant men headed, noisy, cheerful and many unsteady, for the river bank or for the hotel yards to find their horses or their bicycles.

The waggons began to pull out, the horses eager now they were going home. The farmers cracked their long whips at the leaders, flicked their reins and shouted Happy Christmas or Fröhliche Weinachten or Auf Wiedersehen to each other, or they sang or argued with their wives or were sodden quiet. The children lay on the floorboards, in some waggons alongside their paralytic fathers, while the eldest boy or even the eldest girl took the leathers. The dogs, hungry and sullen, ran between the back wheels and snapped at each other.

Jamie watched them go from the mango tree, as he always had, though he seldom climbed it these days. He was too big and the highest perch among the topmost leaves no longer held him. Watched them merge with the surrounding scrub and leave a drifting dust that took long to settle in the golden evening. The hills captured the sun. The darkening town huddled closer as the hot day faded. The high whispering of wild ducks heading for the swamps of Saxony, the shuddering wing-rush of swans, brought a new coolness, a new mood. And down in Chinatown, where the rice was cooking in iron pans, the women were putting up the shutters.

Jamie had risen long before daylight as others were lighting candles and kerosene lamps in distant farmhouses and boys were searching wet paddocks for reluctant horses. He had taken his axe and joined the men among the clean smell of dripping gums and damp earth as they cut and stacked, their calls and laughter ghostly in the quarter dark. He had always loved this day, back into the misty incoherence of childhood. Loved its smells, its sounds, its movement, its excitement. This world of black scrubs and sandspits and olive mangroves was the only one he knew. He belonged as a leaf belongs, as a stream belongs to the slopes where it is born. He was part of a whole that did not have to be explained. Part of the wonder and the mystery of a life that was as familiar as his grandmother's wrinkled face. But this Eve, for all its magic which in the past he had accepted without question, was different, though he could not explain how or why. A welling breathlessness for all the things he did not understand rose and spread. Outward like stone circles in a pond. And suddenly he felt so overwhelmed by the enchantment of this day, this minute, and with an awful feeling that it could never happen again, that he was close to tears.

As the last dust settled he watched the lamplighter come along River Street and stop outside the big house. As he did every evening, to reach with his crooked pole for the pilot chain. And as the gas lamp spread a glow on the roadway and the well of light spilled over the fence into the garden, he felt again the same alarming tumbling of his blood, a new and restless longing for something without shape or words, for strange places he had never seen, for people he had never met or could never hope to meet. For the first time, as he looked through the leaves and the hanging fruit, he longed for the world beyond the hills of the cattle country, beyond the scrubs and the white earth of the Hungry Country, beyond his grandmother and friends and the town itself, beyond the desolation of voiceless trees that spread endlessly to the south.

CHAPTER TWO

A SHADOW at first across his infancy. A brooding presence in the garden. A scatter of sound where the birds and the wind came from. Only much later was Jamie conscious of the mango tree. Its scaly trunk thicker than a man's body, its feathered flowers gold lightning conductors higher than the house.

The tree was so old and freakish that as a child he feared it and even shunned its shade, but as he came to distinguish every limb and junction he was sure, with that still-bright awareness of children before explanations dull imagination, that it knew him and even liked him.

From one Christmas to the next its behaviour was impossible to predict. In some years, as its flowers withered and dropped their nodules, so that the tree rose from Persian grass, and as the green buttons of fruit appeared, old wounds and fissures in the bark wept a crimson menstruation that smelt of spiced and sweetened turpentine. When this flow was slight most of the fruit withered and dropped in infancy and the mangoes that survived were small and sour, but when the gum oozed for weeks and the tree seemed to be in anguish the lower boughs had to be supported with shortened clothes-props to ease their burden and some of the ripening fruit burst and slow-dripped a scented juice.

From childhood he had climbed the tree straining, with fingernails and skinned knees capped with iodine, for the central fork and on in time to the topmost branch that would support him. Where the wind tore at the leaves and flicked them in his face and he clung in a perilous world of sunlight just above the crown. Where he knew appalled delight, the liberty of wings. Where, far below, a stalking cat was a black or tabby shape gliding unsupported across the grass.

In those early years the tree was a castled turret, a peak above the snowline, the spires of a pirate galleon, the tall rigging of the *Cutty Sark*. A name to remember. His father had never forgotten, so his grandmother had told him, an enchanted hour in his youth when, hardly daring to breathe, he had watched this ship, the sun dusting her topsails, making like a beautiful bird across Moreton Bay for the open sea.

The mango tree was a friend, a challenge, a peace, a game, a place to sulk, a place to sing impossible songs above the strings and flutes of scraping leaves. And as he grew, in that mysterious transition from childhood, a weed seeking the sun, the tree became a dreaming place, a confessional where the winds snatched his words and carried them away and the answers never came back.

From the mango tree he could see beyond the bridge to the island in the river where the sea eagles built their stick nests in the highest forks of the tallest gums, and down river to the bend where the mangroves began and the water was deep and evil with red slicks from the rusting mill. West to the black scrubs, the vines rope ladders to the orchid groves along the canopy, and beyond the scrubs to the hills where the copper outcrops sparkled green along the ridges. And east to the sugar fields that flowed up the slopes of the Mount and poured over and down to the sea, a patchwork of emerald and sour green and lemon on a floor of red and chocolate earth so rich he felt he could eat it.

He could trace how the earth roads searched for the town, feeling along the contours, map making as they curved, and he could see part of the macadamised main street with its single- and double-storey shops and timber houses and hitching rails hung with iron rings and even the drinking trough, never free of waving slime, near the post office where the scarlet cyclone flag was raised above the town when a big blow threatened. And, beyond the post office, the lattice bell tower of the fire station where the hoses fell in maypole streamers to dry after a fire, and the blacksmith's shop in lower River Street which stank of horses and steaming piss and red metal and rusting plates and old shoes and where, from afar, hammer and shoe and anvil and asthmatic bellows made a whispering tinkering on hot afternoons that sent him to sleep.

Nearer home, and beyond the big sideyard with its long stables, buggy-house and feed-room under a weeping fig that trailed Chinese boughs to the iron roof, and near the fowl-house draped with Morning Glory and Dutchman's Pipe, the mango tree overlooked part of the Royal yard where Peter Ma Chu, in white apron to his black slippers, stalked beyond bloody wire, snatching with the speed of a native cat and slitting with a flick of his steel-worn knife. So that for ten minutes every morning a pandemonium of frightened cackling and fowl shrieks and splashing bodies and clotted dying that sent cold sniggers like the shudders on the shoulder of a horse up and down Jamie's back. While next door the back of the Commercial where Bandy Mac, the yardman, spoke Scots that few could follow and a soft Gaelic which all the horses understood, so that even the wildest colt with flaming eyes and razor hoofs nuzzled his hand. Bandy Mac lived in one of the lofts, beside the cottage that housed the Commercial's maids, and every Saturday night he drank himself into mournful song that ended in a tear of vomit and a silence that lasted until next day when he emerged, filthy and unapproachable, to wash under the well handpump in the middle of the yard, put on clean clothes and sweep the stables.

The mango tree was Jamie's present but his grandmother gave him his past, chipping it into fragments from the shadowy rock, recreating it from a time more remote to him than the Middle Ages which at least had castles and minstrels and longbowmen to give it some validity.

Grandmother was hard and straight as a stringybark with a high forehead and a sea eagle's nose. She had inherited it from some distant de Bergerac but claimed she had broken it in her youth when a fresh broken horse had taken her into a tree. She was so tall and flat that in profile she seemed even taller, and her bright eyes, grey as slates but smeared from too much seeing, were half open windows in a long Celtic head wrapped in clinker grey. Stern eyes that judged God and man and at times found both wanting.

In the short northern winter, when the farmers lit long lanes of fire against the frosts, she dressed in thick black but in summer in grey with white spots, and always in white on Christmas Eve and Christmas Day. Her black shoes were what was known as sensible. Where her breasts had once parted, she wore a large cameo, with the head of Diana the Huntress in bold relief, or a heavy brooch of interwoven gold which held a bloodstone that mirrored Jamie's face, and on the little finger of her left hand a gold ring with a pale blue stone, almost the shade of winter sky, engraved with a griffin. It had been her husband's. She had put it on after he had died from apoplexy at thirty-nine on the drawing room carpet and had never been able, because of a rheumatic finger, to get it off, although she still tried with oil and soap and once with fish guts because Tom the fish-o-man had told her it was more slippery than an eel.

Jamie never saw her, except in bed, without a high collar of fine net held implacably upright with little posts of whalebone. And he remembered her saying once, in one of her moods of earthy frankness that set her apart from others in the town who were not accustomed to such honesty, especially from a woman, that no woman's neck or the backs of her knees should be seen in public after she turned forty. Until she died, Jamie never knew her age, although she wasn't as ancient as he imagined, but when he was a child, and even much later, she seemed so old that she had moved beyond gender into a time when in some lights her face was that of a weary old man and in others, in those rare moments that seem to exist only in imagination, he could see the shadowy profile of a young girl.

In bed her thin plaits tied with red ribbon framed her face and shrank her skull, so that her eyes seemed to him to be the only part of her that was still alive. They seemed to watch from the parchment on the pillow, seeing into him and through him when she had a migraine, as he brought her water and one of her special powders. White and as big as a half-crown, floating like a misplaced bag of spider's eggs. He never saw her drink the wad and wondered how, with a neck not much bigger than a rooster's, she got it down. He was never allowed to see. 'Now clear out, Sonny Jim.' A command.

When Jamie was small he loved and feared her at the same time. Loved her because she was there, because even then he knew they belonged in some special way, and he absorbed some of her strength and courage and her energy that never seemed to weaken. Feared her for her sternness and her rejection when she no longer needed him or felt the urge to be alone. But in time the fear and love merged and did not need a name. Unspoken, for so many things. The cool firm touch, when he was sick, of her twisted hands covered in grave marks, her poetry voice when she read to him, the fantasy people she harboured inside her head and the miraculous way she could take them out and make them speak and dance and put them away again.

She was all he knew. His father, who had not married until

17

he was in his forties, had been killed when he was three. His mother had died bearing him. From the time he could first recall, a photograph in his grandmother's room had been his only link with her. A girl with fair hair and a rose in her dress and a smile. Of hope, of humour, of doubt. He never knew. The mother who stared unblinking at him from the silver frame was not quite a stranger. He had talked to her about his first puppy, the Black Prince and the Double-drummer he had caught in the garden, his first day at school, and she seemed to listen and understand. But it wasn't enough. As he grew she became more and more remote, a picture retreating back and back. He discovered when he was very young, when he owned a toy bath with a real brass tap, that his mother and dogs and posts and trees and even some people who were not there talked and answered back and told stories, but they became less and less responsive as he grew until at last they did not reply when he questioned them. From that time, or a little later – it all seemed so long ago – his mother lived in grandmother's crowded room and he seldom glanced at her and never spoke to her again. She was no longer a person. Hardly even a name. Only once, later, did she emerge. Just for a moment. Then she slipped away, never to return. Jamie's father, too, lived in grandmother's room. He had big eyes and a black moustache waxed at the ends and a cowlick that fell over his forehead and a high collar and a pearl in his tie. But it was no use talking to him. He never answered.

Jamie's grandmother had been born along the Murrumbidgee not long after the first fifty years of settlement and had never seen the home or the country her mother had left as a young girl and never gave it a thought. This was her place, she said. Her 'hell and her enchantment'. The other world had ceased to exist, merged into the far northern fogs, the day her mother's black and gold Indiaman, with its silver mermaid figurehead, docked at Sydney Cove. Grandmother was part of her own geography and history and as alone and independent as an albatross at sea.

In mood moments she spoke of the 'lonely mystery' of this, her country, of the 'wild hush' of the bush, a description he never forgot, of the land's 'dark winds' that were for ever trying to sweep the alien white invaders back into the sea. She conceived the land as male, so that he never referred to it, as others did, as 'she'. Grandmother taught him her conviction that it was a land not to be understood through the eyes but only through the senses, and not always then. A land to be felt and appreciated and sometimes loved only by searching for and finding its 'indefinable essence'. To her, he knew, this rare love came only through birth and time and only the perceptive stranger could hope to understand even a little of the tormented beauty of its dust green growth, its red earth, its impossible distances, its hills weary with the intolerable weight of time. From infancy, Jamie had absorbed these ideas, as earth drinks water, and made them his own. At times he imagined he had thought them himself and at others that they might have come on the wind, like drifting grass-seeds from the west, or on clouds from the Coral Sea.

After she became a memory more living than alive, he had found among her papers a few sentences that embraced some of the burning ideas with which she had indoctrinated him.

'How can one understand Christ or Moses except through the emotions?' she had written in her bold slanting hand with a hard horizontal stroke before each full stop. 'How can one understand them except through the majesty of their conviction? So one understands this beautiful country of my birth, which I embrace as a lover, not by looking at it but by feeling, as a blackfellow does, simply part of it. By becoming, inside one's very being, one with its deep vast mystery that will forever influence its people and change them and make them new.'

Jamie remembered, as he sat with the paper in his hands, hearing the clamour of the arched sky and the earth breathing and the rocks stirring under their red counterpane.

There were moments when Jamie felt so close to his grandmother that in his guts was the boiling black-green just before a cloudburst. A suffocation so intense that it was almost too much to bear. And that misty afternoon in Boola Street, when he was nearly twelve, was one of them.

They had just reached the 'Lollystick', the pole on the footpath edge that the barber painted in red and white bands every six months as his trademark, when the whole street started running and they heard 'Bolt!', 'Bolt!' from Preacher's Corner and saw the horse coming. At a gallop, the sulky swinging and bouncing, so that as the horse passed the ironmongery a man dived for its head and the trailing reins but was flung into the gutter, and as it came nearer the wheels skidded on the macadam and the sulky swung again and swerved violently towards them.

Jamie saw it coming and knew it would hit him and couldn't move. He felt no fear. Only a stilled fascination. The big goanna he had once seen edging along a bough, inch by inch, towards a small green tree snake frozen and incapable of movement as it watched the goanna's darting tongue. Until the jaws snapped.

Grandmother saw the danger, only in time. She screamed a warning and pushed him and flung herself after him. Just before the wheel splintered the Lollystick with the report of a mast breaking and was dragged on. As far as the corner, under the gas lamps hanging in a cluster, where the shattered spokes collapsed, the sulky overturned and the horse cannoned into the lamppost and fell.

Now everyone was running towards the wreckage. From the Royal and the Commercial, from the post office and the shops, as Jamie helped his grandmother up and brushed her dress.

'Are you all right?' he asked. His voice unsteady.

'Of course.'

'I couldn't move . . . I couldn't move.' He had to say it.

'I know. It happened to me once.'

And did not speak again as they went towards the wreckage and Jamie saw that the horse, with one shaft across it like a curved spear, was still alive. From where he stood he looked into its eyes and the eyes looked back at him from their blood shocked sockets. Moving a little. Tormented and appealing.

'Move back there – back.'

Big Scanlon, the Police Sergeant, six feet four and eighteen stone who could chop through a log quicker than anyone in the central districts. He bent over the horse, his Irish face brighter red against the black hide. He lifted the head and moved it this way and that and let it go.

'The poor creature', Grandmother said. Almost to herself. The crowd parted and waited, talking in whispers, arguing on the fringe, until the Sergeant returned.

'Move away now', he called, cocking the heavy Colt with a thumb like a chop. 'If you please.'

The people edged back. A few feet. Inches. Not wanting to miss anything. And some slowly licked their lips as if they were thirsty.

He put the muzzle to the horse's ear and at the shattering bark the head jerked almost off the ground and for a second Jamie saw the eyes burn with new life and then the light went out.

'Come', Grandmother said.

Jamie hesitated, trying not to look at the blood, thinking

21

of the eyes, of his mother's eyes in the frame in his grand-mother's room.

'Jamie.'

He turned away and followed her. Still thinking of his mother. For the first time for years. Why, he did not know. Except for the eyes and the dying flare in them.

Later Jamie went to his grandmother's room. She was on her bed, but he knew she was not asleep. Her hands were folded.

'I forgot to say thanks Gran – for pushing me.'

She opened her eyes and smiled.

'Tosh. That wheel nearly made mince pies of both of us.'

He grinned. And felt the tumbling inside.

'I was so scared I couldn't move.'

She stared into his. 'A ram charged me once. When I was knee high to a grasshopper. I heard Father shout but I couldn't move. Not a little finger. I never knew why the ram stopped. Father said it was because I stood still. But I still think it was because I was so small and young and defenceless that the old rascal took pity on me.'

She sat up and patted her hair. 'Everyone is frightened at some time. It's nothing to be ashamed of. But fear of people and things you won't face – that's different. There is nothing ennobling about that kind of fear. It's degrading. It eats through one's very soul-case.'

She had never spoken to him like this before. Like a grown-up. Like she did to Mr Murdock the bank manager when he called. Or the Sergeant. He felt strangely warm and grateful.

'When you are older, Jamie, I hope you will never forget that your most precious possession is your pride as a free man. It doesn't matter who you are or what you are. The proudest and the most fearless man I ever knew was a shearer. Michael Desmond Duffy. He always used his three names. I've never forgotten him. A rough and ready diamond at times. But his own man. He walked the stations like a prince.'

She got off the bed. 'Now go and wash your hands. It's nearly tea time.'

Jamie went to the door. And stopped.

'What is it?' she asked. Sensing the unspoken.

'What was my mother like, Gran?'

She stilled but did not hesitate. 'She was a sweet girl and strong. I loved her. She wasn't afraid of anything.'

'Like the shearer?'

'Just like him . . . why do you ask?'

'I just wondered', Jamie said.

And went out.

When Jamie was young entering his grandmother's room was like lifting a trapdoor to another world, and even when he was older he never completely lost the strange feeling of hushed waiting and mystery as though time had congealed and eyes were watching him. Even when he picked up her possessions, and the room was packed with them, he felt that they were so much part of her, and had been with her for so long, that they knew they were being handled and even resented it.

The room contained a high cedar chest of drawers with mother-of-pearl buttons set in the worn knobs, a mahogany dressing table, a leather-topped desk with a large swing mirror on it, and an iron double bed ornamented with brass lace at the ends and brass shell cones that loosely screwed on the corner posts and mewed and tinkled when she moved.

On the dressing table were her silver-backed hairbrushes, long tortoiseshell comb, shoehorn with staghorn handle, silver buttonhook, eau-de-Cologne, smelling salts that lifted Jamie's head off if he put his nose into the blue bottle, three small Georgian silver boxes, one for pins, one for small buttons and one for throat lozenges which she spat out only half dissolved. For months she forgot to wash this box and the lozenges melted into a brown mess, dried and went hard. The table also held a long glass tray for hairpins, with a silver lid that never fitted snugly, a sandalwood handkerchief container, one of her Christmas presents, a bag of lavender garotted with blue ribbon, and a brass-topped jar filled to the top with the hair she carefully collected from her comb and brushes and refused to throw away because it was part of her.

On the chest of drawers was yet another box, inlaid with cowrie shells, that held the strips of black velvet she pinned round her whalebone collar when she chose to be elegant; a bottle of yellow spirit in which floated a large frayed scorpion that had bitten her sixty years before; and a large hairstone removed from the stomach of a favourite cow. Jamie liked the feel of the hairstone, smooth and cool as polished marble. It made him think of the word eternity. But he had no attachment to the scorpion although he knew by heart the story of the stockman who had lanced the bite with his bowie knife to let out the poison and how Grandmother had watched the blade slice her swollen hand – without flinching and without a tear before she was dosed with laudanum. The chest of drawers held miniatures of her father and mother, painted in Paris in the eighteen-thirties, set in a double ivory frame carved with cherubs, and a faded photograph of her long-departed husband, his face almost submerged in hair, in a suede frame stained and marked by generations of dirty fingers.

Grandmother, her gold-rimmed spectacles perched on the hook of her nose, read the Bible every night in bed, muttering and talking to herself and exclaiming 'Piffle' or 'Dear me' or 'I daresay' and laughing quietly at the dirty bits. And when she was ready to go to sleep she hid the Bible behind her husband's photograph because, as she told Jamie once, it had never been any business of the Almighty what went on in her bed.

But to Jamie the true appeal of grandmother's room was the contents of two larger boxes. One, that she kept on the floor beside the dressing table and would not allow anyone to touch, was an early Victorian writing case, inlaid on the lid with jade chips and ivory. It held, under a velvet covered sliding panel, two silver-topped ink bottles, for red and blue, a real turkey quill since she regarded nibs as newfangled, and little drawers for odds and ends. The box had a secret drawer that jumped open when a knot on the side of the case was pressed, though Jamie didn't discover this for a long time until he opened the drawer by accident and found the hiding place of her six diamond rings, one a fiery stone as big as a fly button.

The other box, a campaign case kept under her bed, held a tangle of ribbons, tired pieces of velvet and satin, shoe and belt buckles, one a carved seahorse in silver, another interlocking hands in jet set with diamond chips, a necklace of pearls in a faded blue satin case, strings of lapis lazuli and semi-precious stones, a book of pressed wildflowers, a packet of letters tied with a frayed pink ribbon, a programme from some forgotten ball with the small pink pencil still attached by a silk cord, a set of gold-washed bottles in a leather case still exhaling rumours of lost perfumes, bags of musk and lavender and mothballs, her mother's black lace bonnet frail with age, a lace shawl heavy with real gold shavings sewn on to the material, and one of silver, and even her going-away dress when she was married. It was torn and parts of the dark green taffeta had faded but it was still intact — wide puff sleeves, fragile waist, lace collar and cuffs. Even under the arms ancient sweat still discoloured the material.

She once put it on for Jamie and though it hung on her skin and bone frame and her own waist could no longer fill it, she looked strangely regal and beautiful and hideous. She piled her hair high and impaled it with bone pins and stood without moving before the long mirror on the far side of her room near the window. When she turned she was crying and he did not know why and could not think what to say.

Grandmother's room smelt of eau-de-Cologne, powder, camphor, tired clothes and Grandmother. Sitting in her lap when he was small, listening to the gurgling sounds inside her, Jamie thought she stank of bird's feathers and mice and boxes of long nails and a little sweat. An odour that made his nostrils snigger and search for more. Sitting her legs was riding a post and rail, but in her spread lap, in the hollow where her children had come from and where they had nestled and been crooned to, was sharing a dark and rewarding secret.

'Stop squirming, grub', she would say, as he was getting comfortable. Jamie would relax and sink and suck in the alchemy that was part of her almost lost battle with age.

'How old are you Gran?' he would ask, the chair smooth on its worn rockers.

'As old as my hair and a little older than my teeth, Sonny Jim.'

While she rocked and her smell became stronger and more exquisitely disgusting as he snuggled against her vacant chest, he learnt wondrous things: toads gave you warts if they peed on you, and pigweed cured warts. Two drops of turpentine eaten on a lump of sugar killed the worms that made your bottom itch. Spider web, especially from the big golden spiders in the garden, was the best thing to stop bleeding. Hiccoughs would go if you closed your mouth, held your nose and swallowed four times, but keys down the back were useless. Fresh cowdung made the best poultice but it had to be hot from the cow. Castille soap and sugar was almost as good, and so was linseed. Two drops of iodine drunk in water relieved rheumatism. A single hair, wound round a mole, made it die and drop off. Tainted water, from a dead frog in a tank, would clear miraculously if a teaspoon of Condy's Crystals was dropped into it. Fresh tomato juice, rubbed on and left to dry, took all the pain from sunburn. Silly women who sat in the sun would look like corpses before they were forty. Headaches would go away if you talked quietly to them, but they got worse if you were rowdy. Eating fish was good for the brain but too much crab kept you awake. Pawpaw was good for the digestion. Alcohol rotted your innards. Thunderstorm rain cured prickly heat. Tickling the pink soles of a young baby sent it dotty. And many many more.

Jamie would feel dreamy as her curiously gentle voice, that at other times snapped like a rat trap, washed over him, but her games, some of them, and stories appealed to him most. She could make houses and tents and faces with paper and string and she loved wire puzzles which bored him, especially when she insisted that they helped people think. She also played 'Peter and Paul' with bits of newspaper stuck with spit to her index nails. But for long she would not tell him, as she chanted, 'Two little dickie birds, sitting on a wall, one named Peter, one named Paul: fly away Peter, fly away Paul, come back Peter, come back Paul', how the birds disappeared and reappeared so mysteriously.

From childhood Jamie had known that his grandmother was part of him and he part of her, but he was also dimly conscious even then that she was only one branch in an unimaginable tree spread over him. As he reached puberty and beyond, and met the families and the strangers she peopled her stories with, he became aware, but only in fragments, muddled moments, splashes of impossible perception, that all these dead people were not really dead and gone but alive now inside his own head. So that the past was now and when he was older that future would be now too. It was all very strange.

27

Jamie touched and smelt and tasted, feeling all and understanding little. Learning was an excitement and an agony. Discovery, frightening and wonderful. He explored with his fingertips. And as he groped among the mists of himself he was overwhelmed at times with the knowledge, mysterious and scary, that in him was something caged and something wild, something of the dark past and something of the light.

'We're not all sinful as the Church claims', Grandmother said one night, turning a page. 'We're all innocent. Only some are more innocent than others.'

He wondered what she was talking about.

CHAPTER THREE

To JAMIE the cool dim house with its vaulted rooms, ceilings moulded with embossed fruit, cedar furniture, heavy dark curtains and hallways lined with satanic cupboards, had always seemed an island from which he sailed on magical voyages.

To a Chinatown made more secretive by the smell of cooking and smouldering sandalwood in back rooms. The road to the coast through fields walled with stone by the kanakas. The track that slipped down to the creek and the shack where Tom the old blackbirder lived. The Professor's tin and cardboard gunyah beyond the town's perimeter. And on to the sullen scrubs upriver. And on again to the hills.

But the half-mile he walked from his first day at school had never lost its mystery. Every inch and crack and mark had meaning. The road was like a puzzle game he played with his grandmother. And the discoveries and inventions were his own, part of the hidden life, too secret to be shared, wrapped in brown paper inside his head and tied with string.

The eight fluted iron posts supporting the verandah of the Royal that took on human form on moonlit nights. The sour patch outside the bar where the devil spewed at Easter. And the spot near it, a darker stain, where a jockey had been hit on the head with a lump of blue metal and killed. The hitching rail just around the corner where the road was scraped by restless horses. The shuttered boarding house with the carved head, which in some lights smiled, above the front door. The house where Grandmother said were 'strange goings on'. The low wall around the doctor's garden, just wide enough to run along in sandshoes, too dangerous in boots. The thirteen steps that had to be made with eyes closed, between the paper shop and the next cross street. The cobbled patch that had to be jumped because it was bad luck to tread on the stones. The circle on the footpath which the boys at school claimed had been marked by Old Nick with a chicken bone. The iron railings that cried like violins but only when rattled with sugarcane. The lamppost that had to be tapped three times to appease the evil spirits because it had fallen on a calm night and killed a woman. The cottage set back from the street where a woman had chopped up her lover with an axe and where the bloodstains could still be seen. The Catholic Church with its white Virgin outside, the Church of England with its green spire and leadlight windows, the Presbyterian Church of plain God-fearing board, and all in a group lowering suspiciously at each other like family enemies at a wake.

Jamie soon learned, from listening to his grandmother who would have raised the sword, and used it, to defend the Kirk, that the town revolved around these three buildings. Around those who were C of E who regarded themselves as superior to others, around the Scots who were the only respectable folk, and around the Romans, or the 'Micks' as they were generally called, who were people you did not know, like Lutherans and Methodists, except if you did business with them. To Jamie the Micks coming out of their church looked just like anyone else, but they were still beyond the pale, wherever that was, though their church had the most pleasant smell of all the religious buildings. Like the joss house at Chinese New Year.

To Jamie, the churches meant little more, as he grew, than the collective boredom of Sunday School and the hours he was forced to spend each year, under his grandmother's stiletto eye, designing for the Presbyterian bazaar the word 'Love' or 'Faith' in large Gothic script, to be framed and hung in the Classic Penmanship Section between the Most Suitable Text and Original Drawing (Pencil). It was an annual disappointment to his grandmother that only once did he succeed in gaining not even a third prize but a despised 'Commended'.

At the end of that half-mile, a living map in Jamie's head, was the school he first attended and where he spent what seemed to be his first two thousand years. A single-storey building once painted railway tan, it spread its peeling timbers on one side of a wasteland of red clay empty of grass or trees or shade, with a drain along the opposite side choked with weeds and icy with slime, that became a white river during the rains.

In front of the building, a faded Union Jack topped the flagstaff during school hours after the pupils had saluted it at nine o'clock, sung *God Save the King* in quavering voices and swung Indian clubs for twenty minutes led by Miss Jorgensen who had no bust but great skill.

The school house, unlined under an iron roof that let in splinters of sky and every drip, groaned and cracked in the long summer. Even the desks were often too hot to touch and the inkwells, blocked with blotting paper and beetles and broken slate pencil, dried overnight. But in the short winter the children shivered and wiped their snotty noses with their sleeves as they sucked eucalyptus balls and longed for the playground where they could run themselves warm. The long desks and forms were so heavily carved with names, initials and dirty words by former pupils that they were nailed and reinforced with boards in many places. Even this did not prevent them from collapsing with a crash the whole school enjoyed, and many a desk was encouraged to crumble with the secret and soundless manipulation of a sharp penknife.

The youngest children, who occupied one end of the building, progressed to the left with petrifying slowness until they disappeared at thirteen equipped with a primary education but without having seen a beautiful picture or heard one stimulating idea since childhood. The system's only advantage Jamie realised long afterwards, was that it taught spelling faultlessly. Letters and words were chanted so often and with such monotony that they were imprinted forever, so that he never forgot how to spell even useless words like ornithorhynchus.

The headmaster's ink-stained desk was on a low dais to the front and in the centre of the schoolroom and on the wall behind was a flat glass case holding shells and powdery seaweed and seafans, all red with dust, and another case from which leered a stuffed flying fox, a mangy possum and an assortment of parrots, faded and sad. Between the cases hung a large map of England and another of the world with the Empire all in red, and below were shallow shelves holding bottles of Stephens ink, boxes of yellow-coated chalk and piles of grey slates that stank of old spit. Below again were two racks. One held feather dusters which the junior and senior monitors used each morning, while the rest of the school swung clubs, to beat the desks so that the dust jumped and sparkled in the shafts of sunlight through the broken windows and then settled complacently in the same place. This was known as 'desk bashing'. The other rack displayed five lawyer canes of different lengths and thickness. They were the headmaster's private property. He was an expert.

Old Murph was probably in his late fifties but to Jamie he seemed even older than his grandmother, if that was possible. He was tall and whispy with thin grey hair which he brushed back and left to die on the edge of a bald patch with a bump like a boil in the middle. His moustache sagged below the corners of his mouth and in moments of indecision he tugged his short pepper-and-salt beard. He had brandy eyes and a top set of tobacco-stained teeth that dropped and clacked against his lowers when he became excited. He also had a habit of pushing his steel-rimmed spectacles on to his forehead and forgetting them, so that when the inevitable search for them began his class would pretend they were on the floor or under their desks. He dressed in baggy serge, the coat-front engrained with chalk and his fly copper with urine, a soft collar that drooped in the heat, a black tie on which chalk and food stains made dull paisley designs and heavy boots that he blacked on Sundays but did not brush for the rest of the week. On official occasions, including the annual visit of the inspector, he wore black trousers, a tail coat with silk lapels green with time, and a batswing collar and a frayed black tie fixed to his shirt with an opal stickpin.

Through most of his schooldays, before he went to high school, Jamie sat between Chow Hing and Jack Hatch. Chow was a dark Cantonese whose father had a small general store in Chinatown. He had perfect teeth and hair as coarse as pig bristles. He was so strong that he could wrestle and master two boys of his own size at once, but he had violent moods when, if teased, he would twist the nearest arm he could grab and had to be prised off his victim before the arm broke. At the shout, 'Chow has a yellow cock', he would become uncontrollable. Then all the boys would hold him down and take it out and spit on it to prove it was just like their own, if a little lemon tinged. Jack Hatch, whose father was a drunken pig farmer, carried the smell of the sty on his seldom washed clothes. He was Stinker from his first day. He never seemed to mind. Dull-witted and a ponderous talker, he was always threatening to run away from the father who often beat him and the school where he was permanently at the bottom of the class. He didn't hate school itself. He hated what he called the 'learnin''. At every other activity he excelled. The fastest runner, the best footballer, the finest stalker when before school Jamie and Stinker and the others played Bobbies and Bushies or Cowboys and Indians among the weeds along the drain. He was also the best cockfighter and was middle man at highcockalorum who took most of the weight when his team went down in a line out from the fence and the other team ran and jumped on their backs and added wriggling, crawling and swaying to their combined weight to make the down team collapse and have to bend again. He was good at so many things – tip cat and big ring and triangle and tops and making kites and yabbying. Everyone liked him.

Stinker, despite a black eye or a bruised ear from his father, would be placid for weeks. Then Jamie would notice the first ominous signs. Stinker would not talk or respond. He would sit motionless and stare at the blackboard, so that Jamie knew he looked through it and far beyond. Then he would play with his hands, nervously twisting and pulling his fingers and bending his left thumb back until it touched his wrist. And when he wrote on his slate the letters or numbers would wave and sprawl and some of them were back to front. When this happened Jamie and Chow would exchange glances and nod. At the dinner hour or perhaps the next day Stinker would be gone and he would wag for a couple of days or for a week or more. Then he would return to school, calm again and glad to see his mates, and for days they would hear of his adventures, beyond the rapids or how he had penetrated deep into one of the scrubs and found a bum-stinger tree or had killed one of the big brown snakes that would uncoil and attack if you got them angry. Old Murph would reach for a cane and give him twelve on each hand and another lecture and Stinker would listen with eyes measuring sun and shadow beyond the door. Jamie and the others all knew what six was like but few ever got twelve and never on both hands. Old Murph was fastidious. His thickest lawyer left pale bruises across the fingers and sometimes on the thumbs but the hand quickly became numb and the jar did not hurt much, until later. But all feared the thin lawyer that whipped and sang. For talking or cheating or going to sleep on one of those anaesthetic afternoons of heat and droning voices and slow farts and the song of blowflies and the oily scrape of pencils on filthy slates, Old Murph would line up a class, carefully select the thin cane and, placing himself in front of the first boy in line, his boots wide apart, his free hand under his coat behind his back to give him added balance, would first practise, and the whistle through the thick air was one of the most menacing sounds Jamie remembered. When Old Murph was ready he gave everyone six on one hand, moving down the line like a dancer, swaying to the rhythm of arm and body and heels. When the class filed back to their seats every stroke had been exquisitely aimed. Not a mark. Not a bruise that showed. But Jamie felt that the tips of his fingers, and only the tips, had been sliced off with a vegetable knife.

Jamie did not resent this punishment. He accepted the cane as he accepted a head cold or a cut toe, to be endured and forgotten. In a vague way he even liked the caning because it was a challenge and it relieved the bleak hours at school. But Black Friday was different. A new dimension. It made him feel suddenly older and baffled. It lay like a stain across his memory that never completely disappeared.

Stinker was playing the wag again, his first lapse for many weeks. A sugar ship was in and he had been seen by some pimp fishing from the end of the wharf. Old Murph sent two of the senior boys, the biggest and bullies, to find him and bring him back, and the first the class knew of this was after the dinner hour when Stinker was dragged in after a last scuffle on the verandah.

The teachers tried to ignore his arrival and continued their work, but the pupils paid no attention. They stared open-mouthed at poor Stinker and in the silence one of the youngest boys suddenly whimpered. Jamie watched. Sick and helpless. Knowing that something awful was about to happen. Old Murph reached for his thickest and heaviest cane and, grabbing Stinker by the collar of his khaki shirt, lashed him on his backside and on his legs. Stinker jerked and writhed as the cane hit with a flat dry sound against his shorts, as it cracked against his bare legs. But he did not cry out. Not a yelp or a whimper. And the very soundlessness of his thrashing seemed to act as a catalyst. Something inside Old Murph seemed to snap. He attacked Stinker with added fury. He dragged him over the front desks and beat him on the back, the head, the backside until Stinker jerked free and fell. He dragged him to his feet and continued to thrash him and as the cane beat against him the most terrible cry Jamie had ever heard split the schoolroom. A scream mixed with too much spit. Not a cry of pain but an agony of protest, appeal, outrage.

Now the younger children were screaming and sobbing as Jamie saw Miss Jorgensen sag like a bundle of old clothes thrown in a corner. A master shouted and waved his arms. A child fell off the end of his form and yelled. Jamie covered his face. Then he was standing, shouting, 'No', 'No', just as Stinker, his legs striped brick red against the tan, his shirt ripped, shook himself free, ducked another swipe and with a round arm swing hit Old Murph on the side of the head. The headmaster's ear opened like a rose and blood splashed down his cheek. He dropped the cane and put a hand to his head. He looked dazed and for the first time sane. As Stinker turned and ran, Jamie ran after him and from the verandah watched him sprint across the schoolgrounds. As he reached the far gate the vomit was in Jamie's mouth and all over the boards and he was running too, through the main gate and along the half-mile that led to River Street and up the back steps and into the big kitchen where he hid all the horror of that day against Pearl's large breasts and felt the woman comfort come through to him and her arms about him and her rough voice soothing.

'There there now. What's got inter yer?'

He told her, sobbing against her smell of butter and sweat and starched apron, and when he had no more to tell she kissed him on top of the head and sat him at the scrubbed table and poured home made lemon juice, with a chunk of ice from the block in the ice chest, and cut a piece of walnut cake from the tin in the pantry.

'Youse 'ave ter learn', Pearl said, as she finished the potatoes, 'yer in a cruel world. Look what them foreigners did ter our Jesus. But some people is kind. Yer granny's treated me right.'

He felt better. Just watching her as she poked the fire, took a potcloth and lifted a stove lid and put the iron pot of water over the licking flame. Just sitting there, part of the warmth and comfort from the smell of the wood in the black polished range, of cooking and carbolic from the lead sink and the clean dry smell of sandsoap from the scrubbed table where the pastry was rolled.

When his grandmother returned from a School of Work at the Presbyterian church hall, he told her. Every detail he could remember. She heard him through without a word. She could see how upset he was.

'Stinker was beaten something awful', he repeated.

'So I hear', she said. 'From all over town.'

And seemed to be deciding what to say. How much to say.

'The school council has had a meeting. That is my under-standing. The headmaster claims the reports were grossly

37

exaggerated and the teachers agree Stinker deserved a good whipping.'

'But Old Murph hit him on the face', Jamie said.

She heard the appeal. 'Once?'

'Many times. And on his nut.'

'That drunken old . . . .'

She did not finish. She stared into the garden.

'I believe he is to be expelled. From what you and others have told me I don't agree with the decision. Downright foolish. That's what I call it. But unfortunately nothing can be done about it.'

She rested a hand on Jamie's head.

'I'm sorry for Stinker, too. And for justice.'

Jamie went down the steps and sat under the mango tree. Too dejected to climb into its friendly branches. The events of the day elbowed each other inside his head. The cane bouncing on Stinker's skull, his terrible cry. The pictures blurred and ran together. He tried to separate them. Old Murph was off his rocker. Yet they believed him. Old Murph had told a lie. Yet the teachers who knew he had lied had sided with him. Stinker had played the wag but he was not bad. Just not very bright.

A weight seemed to press down on him. He felt helpless and alone in the fading light of that awful day. He began to cry. But too tired to make a sound. A welling that started at the bottom of his guts and never came out. He cried for Stinker and for himself. For all who had lied. But mostly he cried for the new and terrifying knowledge that day had brought and for the suffocating weight of the world.

Pearl found him. 'Don't take on so bad. Things is never so bad they can't git worse. Now go an' wash yer face an' do yer 'air. It's Irish stew fer tea. Yer like that.'

And later, when she was ironing, and he wanted a knife to sharpen his pencil, she said, more to herself than to Jamie:

'Females speaks what they think. That's why thems'll never run th' world. Men stick together. That's why them school gints went along with yer teacher – even if they knewed he wuz tellin' woppin' fibs.'

CHAPTER FOUR

PEARL was nearly as broad as a door. She had huddled eyes, a protruding upper lip, tired brown hair scraped to a tight little bun, a sallow skin pitted about the chin from early pimples.

But Jamie never saw the grotesque body, the untidy face. To him she was not ugly or plain but warm and kind and generous. As long as he could remember. She was just Pearl who had been with them always and was as much a part of his life as Grandmother.

Only years later did he know her background. How her father had carried his swag north many years before, from a place with an impossibly long name she had once written down for him and he had learnt to spell. He never forgot that it had eight o's and three l's, not four. Woolloomooloo. On paper it looked like water running over stones.

How her father had run off with a wandering knife sharpener's daughter and drunk himself out of every job. And how, not long before he was killed in a drunken brawl with cane knives, he had raped Pearl when she was thirteen. Jamie also knew, from his grandmother and from others, that her brother had been killed in the Boer War, that her mother had deserted her and that at fourteen she was on her own, working in boarding houses and hotels and once in a parson's house before he and his family returned to England and later as a cook in a timber camp where she thrashed a bullocky with an axe handle after he had grabbed her in the lean-to kitchen and torn off her clothes. In another town they still told the story of the naked Pearl, her body covered with filth from the earth floor where she had struggled and slithered in the dirt and fat to hold herself away from him, her hair loose, her breasts bobbing angrily, as she broke free and belaboured her attacker and left him almost senseless before the foreman disarmed her.

Jamie could just remember when she came to River Street. His grandmother had found her in the park, dry-eyed but lonely when jobs were scarce. And Pearl had paid for the position and home – the only real home she had ever known – with devotion and work that would have killed most men.

Pearl worked for twenty-three shillings a week, which everyone who employed maids complained was pandering to the working class and ruining the market for domestics. She had Saturday afternoon off once a fortnight and one Sunday free in every month, which was more than most domestics were allowed. She rose at six o'clock, made tea on a primus stove and brought it to Jamie and his grandmother. She was seldom in bed before ten. She did all the rough work, the sweeping, dusting, scrubbing and wax polishing of the red linoleum which Jamie enjoyed sliding on, and all the food peeling and preparing, though Grandmother did some of the cooking. Pearl laid the dining table and served the food, and did all the washing up and silver polishing and knife cleaning and sharpening and wood carrying for the kitchen range and for the fire in the drawing room in mid-winter. She emptied the slops and cleaned, with hot soapy water, the flowered chamber pots. She also made the beds and hooked up their coarse mosquito nets which no amount of washing could stop from yellowing with dust and time.

On Mondays she began work at five o'clock. Filled the big copper boiler in the laundry by bucket from the undrinkable water tank that was full of wrigglers, and then lit the fire

41

before she sliced, with a blunt knife, half a bar of barilla into the warming water. With the help of the boiler stick, its end as frayed as an old toothbrush and soft from too much soap and hot water, in a temperature of about one hundred and twenty degrees in summer, a bleached scrubbing board and her own scarlet hands she did the family wash, squeezed it through the mangle, hung it out, pulled it down into the old Chinese basket, carried it to the kitchen and ironed every article, and in time to prepare and serve the evening meal, wash up and dry the dishes and silver, and mend a sheet or one of Jamie's shirts before going to bed.

She was never ill, not even a cold though once she had the sniffles. She never complained, never lost her temper, although if Jamie fussed-up her kitchen or left finger-marks she would become cross. She smiled rarely and never laughed except when Jamie tickled her. Then she would sink helpless to the floor in her long white apron and become hysterical, a wild choking laughter punctuated, when she could get her breath, with 'Git on wiv yer'.

Pearl walloped Jamie only once and he knew he deserved it. He was playing with school friends behind the dunny, in a bamboo grove in a corner of the back garden, hosing lizards on the fence and seeing how high each boy could pee, when they heard Pearl close the door and settle. Dared by one, who gave him a stick, he silently opened the small back doors, which Dismal Dan used to change the tins on Friday nights, and froze at the extraordinary sight of her seat-encircled bottom staring sternly down at him. Jamie wanted to run but, in a moment of panic, he poked. The white bottom exploded and Pearl, her skirt and petticoat to her waist, and her long blue bloomers still on the way up, attacked. She moved so quickly he still held the stick. She didn't speak but a frozen anger masked her face. She grabbed him by an ear, led him behind the stables and with the stick lathered his backside.

42

'An' now yer bloody little larrikin', she said, 'if yer says sorry ter me in th' kitchen, I won't tell on yer to yer granny.'

Pearl kept her word. It was yet another bond between them. But the only time he ever saw her almost speechless was the episode in the mango tree.

The five maids who worked at the Commercial lived in a cottage in an enclosed garden at the bottom of the hotel yard and the mango tree overlooked this garden. Jamie and two of his mates were up the tree one Sunday afternoon, hidden by the leaves, when four of the maids came from the cottage wearing long pink bloomers and nothing else except for the hair down their backs and over their shoulders. But the fifth girl was naked. Her hair was long, black and rippling, but her bush was burnished gold, curled in ringlets.

Jamie gripped the frail bough and tried not to make a sound but felt sure the girls could hear him breathing. One of the other boys sniggered but not loud enough to cause discovery. All the girls Jamie had seen had clothes on and he couldn't keep his eyes off the ringlets and didn't want to. Ted Larkin at school had black hair and a red bush but he never knew it happened to girls. He tried to control the shaking of the bough as the maids stood first in a group and then a close line while the naked girl, her bottom towards him, took photographs with her Box Brownie. Jamie knew girls had breasts. He had looked the word up in the dictionary and he had seen naked pictures in the *History of All Nations* his grandmother bought every month in instalments. But he did not know before that they were all shapes and sizes, even like home-made ice cream with cherries on top. When the naked girl finished taking her photograph, after much posing and laughter from the others, and turned towards him, so that the sun glinted for a moment on the gold ringlets, his hand shook so much that he lost his balance. One moment the astonishing ringlets were framed below him. Then he fell, scratching and clawing, and bouncing off lower boughs, until he landed at the base of the trunk head first into a half-hogshead permanently kept there and spilling over with festering mango stones and old skins that broke his fall and saved his neck. And as he landed he still heard the shrill laughter from across the fence.

The crashing in the mango tree, like a brumby through undergrowth as Grandmother said, brought her and Pearl. It took them a long time to get the slime and sting from his eyes and the stink of rotting fruit from his hair. Only then did Grandmother demand an explanation. Jamie knew that if he didn't tell she would find out, somehow. She always did. So he told all. And as she listened her ancient face puckered and twisted. She broke into harsh laughter.

At last she said: 'The lesson, Sonny Jim, is that if you have to be a Peeping Tom don't be up a tree.' She began to laugh again. 'What you've seen won't do you any harm. It could even be good experience one of these fine days.'

Jamie couldn't see what experience he could get from falling out of the mango tree because he had looked at naked sheilas. He kept quiet.

But Pearl didn't laugh.

'It's them wages o' sin come 'ome ter roost', she snapped. And walked away. And wouldn't talk to him for two days.

On her rare afternoons off Pearl slept and complained next day that too much sleep was 'bad fer th' body'. But on her monthly free Sundays she dressed carefully in a dress Grandmother had bought for her, with a lace collar added, put on a hat decorated with red glass cherries, dabbed a smear of powder on her chin, and left for the day. Grandmother never knew where she went and never inquired. But riding his bike through the East End, the poorest part of town, Jamie saw her leaving a cottage. Grandmother soon found that Pearl's aunt lived there and that Pearl paid the four shillings a week rent from her wages.

Pearl was the only private maid in town who wore a cap. Grandmother insisted. Starched with a broad band in front and with wings on top like a Viking, Pearl liked it, although she had grumbled at first. She wore it only at what everyone called dinner; at one o'clock. This was a custom, inherited from the time of the Queen, which demanded that men needed a big meal during the day to keep up their strength and to keep out the heat.

Dinner was served by Pearl from the big sideboard, but only after Grandmother had solemnly cut the meat, muttering just loud enough to be heard that someone had again neglected to take the carver to the steel. Dinner was a fairly silent ritual, punctuated when Jamie was young by stabs from Grand-mother's sharp thumb on his spine and hisses – 'Sit up straight, you young devil.'

But tea at half-past six, or supper as it was called if there were guests, was more relaxed. Grandmother ignored his elbows on the table and seldom charged him with 'slumping again like a dirty sugar sack', though she made spot checks of his nails and, if they offended, would snap, 'You could grow a bushel in that lot.'

Pearl's monthly free Sunday was a special day, but only in summer, to Jamie. No food was cooked and the evening meal was ginger sandwiches, fruit and coffee on the grass under the mango tree, though it was impossible to remain there much beyond early twilight. Grandmother, whose hearing was as acute as Jamie's, would sniff the hot air, cooled and sweetened a little with mignonette and mint and lemon and mango gum, and say, 'Here they come.' The first sound was little more than a tremor in the air that rapidly increased until, as Grandmother said, the converging millions of mos-quitoes from the swamps, the scrubs and the river mangroves

45

advanced like 'ten town bands'. Jamie knew them all – the small black stingers, the larger tigers with black and yellow stripes, the big Scotch Greys whose sting, worse than a pin stab, itched for hours. Even a bucket of smouldering cow-dung, mature and suffocating, would not keep the mosquitoes away, and the retreat to the house would begin, led by Grand-mother. She would rise from her cane chair, smooth down her long dress, and, from the superior heights of her New South Wales birth, proclaim, 'This may be the Queen's land but it's still blackfellow country.'

Even inside the house, despite the screens, the mosquitoes could be kept at a distance only through a blue haze from smouldering Chinese 'koksek' spirals – bright green, thick as a meat skewer and made, so everyone said, from tiger's dung and dragon's blood – and if a window or a door was left open the elephant and death's head beetles, the big brown beetles and the small blacks, and every moth in creation would pour in, like women at a sale, and die gloriously against the red-hot mantles of the popping gaslights, or pepper the ceiling, or land on pictures and furniture with a woosh of blurred wing-cases.

Jamie's bed was on a side verandah where sleep was im-possible without heavy nets tightly tucked. He liked the nets. They made a cave into which he crawled. He felt secure. On these special Sundays he would lie waiting for Pearl to return and bang the back door at nine o'clock. Listening to the shrilling of the mosquitoes probing for his blood through the net holes or the oboe note of an elephant beetle passing through in laboured flight or the splash of flying foxes in the mango tree when the fruit was ripening. When he was very young he would lie, rigid and afraid, as they snarled and bickered and snapped at each other, hanging head down by their hooked wings like black bundles wrapped in the dark-ness of the tree. Jamie thought they were witches and looked for broomsticks in the garden. He once asked his grandmother why he could never find any.

'Some of the ladies of the town own them', she said. But the women he studied in Boola Street did not look like witches and never carried broomsticks.

He didn't believe all the things Grandmother told him after that.

CHAPTER FIVE

JAMIE ran into the shining morning, feeling he had grown another skin. Saturday. It held the weeks apart, poured excitement into the air. Like the smell of cherry mangoes, the taste of cold guavas picked before the sun. The hills were closer. The river winked with light at the bottom of the garden. The birds argued more harshly and more sweetly. As if they and every living thing had emerged from their hiding places or taken wing into a day without horizon.

A time to fly a Chinese fish kite with crimson scales or a big bender that needed all the bows he could make for its tail from his grandmother's ragbag, or to circle boomerangs in glinting parabolas beyond the fig-trees or to fish from the river rocks with bamboo pole and copper line and pink prawns white with brine.

To watch the farmers coming into town, to stroke the coats of horses with his eyes, to feel the warmth of greetings shouted across the street, to know the excitement of dogs, away from humans, sniffing and yapping among their own kind.

To listen to familiar cries. The metallic call of the clothes-prop man, his wares, still with the bark trailing from them, balanced across his shoulder, the 'Fish-O , Fish-O' from Tom as he stopped outside every house in River Street, the auction-man in the long grey dustcoat who carried a red flag and swung a heavy brass handbell and shouted announcements in gibberish.

To think about what went on beyond the sky or why the

clouds had different colours or what would happen if the tides stopped turning.

Or, if they were in town, to stand on the corner beside the Italian musicians who called him, with dark familiar eyes, 'Young Joey'. They seemed to come through town every few months, though it was probably less frequent, following a nomadic pattern like desert Arabs or mountain Turkomans. They set their golden harp, thick with angels and leaves and clusters of fruit, on the pavement outside the Royal bar and folded the faded blue wrapping cloth and laid it carefully on the ground as if it were precious. They were darkly smiling young-old brothers who wore coats with scarlet handkerchiefs knotted loosely at their throats and hair so long that it turned up at the collars and spilled over their ears. One played the harp, stroking and plucking so that even the horses at the hitching rail flicked their ears and trembled. The other played the violin. Music from opera mostly, a word that early had no meaning to Jamie. Gay exciting sounds that fed his blood and made the back of his neck shiver and urged him to sing and dance and beat time, though he never did. Older people would look down their noses at such behaviour and think him silly.

They played to a circle of grinning farmers and their wives and children. And before they moved on to another pitch, near the Commercial and later outside the hospital, Franco, the monkey, the third member of the group, collected the threepenny bits and the coppers with darting fingers. He wore dark blue pants, through which his tail curled, that stank of ammonia since he had to pee somewhere, a short scarlet jacket embroidered with sequins and a red fez held on by dirty white elastic under his chin. Franco reminded Jamie of his grandmother. He carried a tin cup, offering it to onlookers who had not dropped a coin with a menacing chattering and bared teeth that made some of the women squeal and

49

the younger children clutch at their mothers' long skirts. And when he had collected the money he emptied it into the open violin case where the silver lay like small fish in the red water of the velvet lining.

Jamie loved and hated the Italians who brought with them a rumour of the breathing world beyond the black scrubs. As he dropped a penny into Franco's tin he always felt excited and then resentful. Not with the brothers. They were old friends. With the music. The plucked notes that broke from the harp strings and fell to the street like heavy raindrops and left him, in a muddled way as he grew, restless and uneasy.

But Saturday morning, with its hurry and stamping horses and bags dragged from shops with a dry swishing and parcels tossed into carts and sulkies, reached noon and beyond and by one o'clock the town had emptied. By two o'clock, except for the hoofbeats of a late horseman, gripping with drunken knees, the shops were closed, the streets were empty, the town was silent.

A clamouring silence at first. Then of desertion. Like the inside of a derelict farmhouse miles from nowhere. Different from the virginal quiet of early morning or the mysterious subterranean quiet of the dark hours. A silence so deep in Jamie's head that it made him doubt at times that he was still alive. Of hushed birds and golden emptiness made more soundless by the scrape of leaves, stray hammering of a board far off, a shadow stretching like an old man who has sat too long in the sun. A brooding eminence that Jamie could almost touch, a sweet savage loneliness just beyond the tips of his outstretched fingers. And later, for a heartbeat as elusive as the long-tailed turquoise butterflies that froze over the mango flowers, a point of response, an awareness of rest, when Jamie knew that he and the weeds and the sun and the sleeping birds and all things, the town itself, the buildings and everyone in them, were in harmony.

But this moment never lasted. Nothing ever did, as he discovered as he grew. So that it was impossible to decide what was real and what was imagined. Like the boy at school who told stories of weird things that creatured his room at night. The dragon that breathed out glittering diamonds and breathed them in again. The ape-like animal that changed colour and made sounds like soft pistol shots. Descriptions given so quietly and so seriously that all the boys shuddered for more, even though they all agreed that Tommy, who ate handfuls of earth if bribed with a bullseye or a liquorice stick, was nuts.

For Jamie that moment of mid-afternoon repose died as it happened. As the shadows began their sprawl across the garden, along the street, into the river from the northern bank and the island of petrified gums, the afternoon stirred and a new mood elbowed the quiet aside. Soon the air was filled with fleeting things that could not be captured; frail wings of hope and despair, love and anguish, guilt and innocence. And all mixed up like the clutter in his grandmother's box and incomprehensible, yet full of some awful meaning in those dying hours of Saturday afternoon. Fleeting things that at some time, a thousand years away, he would stalk and capture.

But Saturday nights were different. Not part of the same day. They began with the lamplighter carrying his short ladder and his hooked pole. With the pieman whom Jamie never once saw, in all those years, in hard daylight. At six o'clock, summer and winter, the pieman came down River Street, out of nowhere, before he turned into Boola Street. And at midnight he returned, going nowhere. He emerged, lived and died each night and was buried in the day, and Jamie never questioned this metamorphosis. The pieman was as much a part of his experience as Pearl or the big horse-trough near the post office, and Jamie accepted his arrival and his departure without question. He was a habit, a reminder, a constancy. Not unlike a fleeting evening visit of conscience. Jamie never knew his name or troubled to find out. There was no need. The pieman was the pieman who wore white trousers, polished black boots and a long white starched coat buttoned to the neck and, above a smooth pink anonymous face, a cloth cap with a peak just above the level of his eyes. He also wore a handkerchief that was not a real handkerchief but a piece of boiled linen around his throat. Jamie never knew if he was bald, but his hair above his ears and at the back was almost as white as his coat.

The pieman had a box-like handcart fitted with blunt shafts and rests. When he stopped pushing, the cart remained level. As he advanced into town, always punctual, he rang a small bell which brought people from their homes to buy his twopenny pies and to splash them with tomato sauce that he made himself and kept in a large Host Holbrook bottle.

At the big house his pies were scorned. Grandmother said they were only good for telling the time. Pearl said that a good piece of old greenhide was more digestible. But Jamie lusted. He found a penny in the gutter outside the Royal bar and with another he stole from Grandmother's purse he bought a pie further down the street where he could not be seen. Pearl found him near the bird house doubled with indigestion and dosed him with hot bicarbonate of soda until he burped.

'Serve you right', Grandmother said. 'At least you've learnt another of the seven deadly sins.'

Jamie searched the encyclopedia at the School of Arts and found they had nothing to do with pies or indigestion. His disgust with grown-ups grew.

Saturday was also the best night for Old Mick whose cab stank of horse and old leather and decaying horsehair. As the only cabbie in town, he earned more than half his income on Saturday, so that for this one night a week he was almost too busy to think of his piles that most cabbies suffered from, so Grandmother said, because of too much sitting still, too much sitting on wet seats and never going to church. But during the week when, for hours, he slumped like a loosely tied bundle on the rank outside Tucker's Hardware and Wholesale Liquor Store without a fare, asleep or reading 'Aboriginalities' in the *Bulletin* or passing the time of the day with cronies, his temper was uncertain.

Jamie once threw a pad at his sleeping horse, after carefully selecting one near the river, where cows sometimes grazed, that was perfect for throwing. Dry and crisp but still loose inside, so that when it hit another boy's head it broke easily and splashed soft cowsh all over him.

Jamie crept up behind the cab and let the horse have it on the rump. Emperor, who was twenty years old and had once been a racehorse, reared on his hind legs and Old Mick fell off the driving seat crying, 'The end's come, the end's come', until he woke properly, snatched the reins and shouted, 'Whoa, whoa, my beauty' until Emperor settled down. Then he saw Jamie. He grabbed his long carriage whip, with the cracker at the end, which normally stood imperiously upright in its metal sheath, and chased him almost to the river before shortage of breath and his piles halted him.

'I'll have yer knackers yet, yer young devil', he threatened, waving his whip, before limping back to the rank where Emperor, who had been taught to stand, was now dozing. All the way back Old Mick held his backside with one hand and muttered, 'Oh, me bleedin' piles, me flamin' bleedin' piles.'

Jamie followed at a safe distance, cocky, feeling no pity. Not knowing yet that pity is born of pain and compassion, inherited from among the echoes of experience and of time. But he kept out of range of Mick's whip until the cabbie forgot or forgave.

Jamie liked Saturday night, but only the early part of it.

Talk of hurrying feet, passing words flicking across the fence like scraps of paper, splash of perfume in the evening air, elusive and exciting, whisper of long skirts, faces under the lamplight that seemed alarmingly alive and eager. For what? He did not know. Except that ladies were more beautiful at night and all people seemed to change in some mysterious way after dark. Mostly, he liked the gathering excitement when the town's heart beat more strongly.

Once he had put his ear to the ground and heard the earth breathing, the pulse beneath, the hiss and flow of the deep dark, the tumult of digesting rocks. Felt part of everything. Even of people he did not know sitting on their front steps in the evening cool. Of laughter from bug infested rooms. Of shouts in the street.

Once, as the sun went down, he had lain among the sida retusa weeds and had watched a late ladybird in her black and orange suit climb a stalk, flexing her wings in little convulsive flutters as though about to fly, but never flying, just going on, climbing from nowhere to nowhere, until triumphant she reached the top just as a sparrow with one wing flick took her away.

He felt the tears, hot and salty. She was so small and gentle, so beautiful and defenceless. It didn't make sense. At times little did. As he held back, since his grandmother said that only girls cried, he felt in a voiceless way, as he thought of the ladybird in the awful darkness of the sparrow's stomach, the horror of being alive.

When Jamie was just high enough to see over the sill, when he was about eight, he liked to slip out after the evening meal and, unbeknown to his grandmother, walk up and down on Saturday nights amid the wondrous thick and alien smell of onion soup and grilled pork and chook cooked Chinese style, just outside the big open dining-room windows of the Royal and pause and falter on and pause. A shy long enough to stare at the white tablecloths, the starched napkins folded into fans and birds and tents, the silver winking at the gaslight, the cruets like little mosques, the fruit heaped in flowered porcelain bowls, the platters of raisins and nuts and dates, the black suits of the men and their high collars, the hurrying waitresses in tall caps and long aprons tied with broad bows at the back, the naked terrifying shoulders of the ladies.

To Jamie, a room of fantasy people, as indeed they were. With no relationship to the town. They arrived, stayed a few hours or a few days and were never seen again. He wondered in his early years if they were real. For under the smouldering gas globes was a life mystical and unreachable. But something in that room beckoned and some day it would be his. He would be able to reach and grasp it with both hands. Feel it, smell it, even taste it. And know.

And then, as he peered in one evening, a lady with hair as black as a crow saw him and smiled. A slow lips-parted lingering smile he had never seen before. Jamie was so astonished he forgot to duck, as he generally did if anyone inside glanced his way. He stared, his body tight as a pumped football. She lifted a hand and moved her fingers at him so that they danced, and there were rings on them, one a drop of blood on her pale skin. She picked up an apple and tossed it and at the same time her lips spelt 'catch'. The apple came straight to him, through the window and into his hands like an easy catch in slips. He looked at it, polished where the light caught it, and looked again at her. She smiled and he ducked and ran home, dazed, not feeling the pavement, and for weeks he thought of her smile and felt uneasy yet elated as though he had gulped a half-ripe mango and wondered if it would give him the trots. He never ate the apple. He kept it under his pillow. He took it out and felt it in the dark and thought of that smile. Slowly the apple shrivelled and rotted. Pearl threw it away.

55

Saturday night meant people he knew, people he recognised, people who, like the lady in the dining-room, were strangers. Relaxed on front steps or verandahs or above the street at the hotels in wickerwork or canvas chairs, bathing in the evening cool, feeling it soak into their hair and under their arms and into their crotches, resting from the week in the quiet, their stomachs amiable, watching the nervous smoke of pipes spiralling. Families with their dogs wandering disordered along the track above the river, stopping and coming together to gossip with friends, to toss sticks into the river and skim stones, to break apart and move on to the bend and disappear. People in their best clothes; long dresses and big hats with flowers; high collars and stiff cuffs and narrow trousers, even a walking stick or two, promenading from the fire station to the edge of Chinatown and back along the other side of River or Boola Streets. Even the larrikins who crept out of the East End only at night, from beyond the creek, to hold up corner posts and leer at respectable ladies, and even whistle, and later pick up their own girls to finish in the pit at the pictures with their hands up their sheilas' bloomers. To Jamie the larrikins were a tribe apart. They did not even dress like anyone else but wore bum-freezer coats with wide lapels and bell trousers that flapped and the pockets of their coats were cut on a slant, with the corners stitched with silk darts like miniature arrowheads. They wore striped shirts and striped ties that Grandmother said were so loud they could be heard a mile away.

Grandmother knew everyone in town and would even stop and talk to the larrikins. But Pearl had much more rigid views. Jamie could never understand why there were people it was possible to know, people to recognise and people not to know. Those who could be spoken to freely, those to whom one bowed or raised one's hat and those one ignored. But after he reached his teens he tried to compromise between his grandmother's egalitarianism and Pearl's rigidity. Yet once, when Pearl saw him talking to a girl from one of the shops, she spoke sternly.

'Yer shouldn't talk to them people. It's not right fer yer.'

'But she was at school – before I went to the High', Jamie protested.

'That's as maybe. But she's not yer kind.'

Yet one night his grandmother said to him, so that he was sure she had been talking to Pearl or had overheard her:

'With some people, whatever their class, you will never have anything in common. These you ignore. But one day you will thank God we have never had aristocrats or peasants in this country. It is what makes us different from the tired old world. It is our one great hope for the future – if men are wise.'

'Are they?' he asked.

'No', she said. 'Men most of the time behave like fools. But here at least they have a chance of not repeating the horrible mistakes of history.'

Saturday night meant the one-night-a-week pictures, which everyone called 'the pitchers'. In a hall like the inside of a whale behind the fire station and the only place in town with electric light. There, in its own shed, an engine with a huge flywheel and flapping belt generated an anaemic light. To Jamie the engine had a mysterious life of its own and he often sucked the exciting smell of hot oil and metal and acid while loitering before posters of William S. Hart holding a smoking Colt and staring sternly at distant tepees or the dark bold eyes of Pola Negri that made him feel uncomfortable. Envious of the boys who on Mondays described the latest cowboy picture or the soupy bits from the dramas. Grandmother denounced the pictures as 'Yankee rubbish' or 'degrading tripe', so Jamie was never allowed to go, even to the two o'clock matinee where the pit whistled and stamped and threw half sucked humbugs and bullseyes and burst paper bags and spat because it was grown up. Not until he was nearly fifteen and then only with a group from the high school to see a highly commended picture about the war which condemned the Huns as 'fiends in uniform'. As it was his first, Jamie almost peed himself with excitement, but there were so many delays that he wondered if he would ever see the real picture. The man who played the musical effects on the piano arrived late and unsteady and had to be bribed with a small bottle of whisky before he would start, and the engine stopped twice in the first ten minutes and the audience stamped and whistled in the dark. Jamie, watching the silent figures moving behind what looked like a curtain of heavy rain, and not being able to read all the subtitles before the next lines appeared, was not sure at any time what the picture was all about. Except near the end when the German counter-espionage officer, fierce in spiked helmet, Prussian moustache and Iron Cross, lurked with dreadful intent behind a garden seat and heard the hero and heroine, both gallant British spies, arrange how to get the Kaiser's war plans back to London. And the final scene when they were suspended by their thumbs in the grey German prison and then led into a courtyard, with snow on the ground, to face the firing squad after scornfully refusing to have their eyes bandaged. Jamie liked the last scene best when the effects man played the Dead March, with many wrong notes, as an officer with drawn sword gave the order to the firing squad – just like in drawings he had seen of Nurse Cavell – and through the smoke the blood welled from the black bullet holes in the foreheads of the hero and heroine as they fell to the ground locked in each others arms. As the lights went on, reluctantly, since the engine had missed and coughed during the performance, most of the women and girls in the audience were holding handkerchiefs to their eyes or were sniffing. Jamie thought they were soppy.

After the pictures on Saturday nights the town made for Comino's to eat black mud-crabs that turned brick red when boiled or grilled trumpter or steaks heaped with onions while Georgi, his coat off and gold watch-chain hung with medallions across his waistcoat, his thin hair plastered in strands across his polished skull, moved among the tables, laughing and shouting orders, while Momma, only five feet one inch high and almost as wide, and strapped in corsets that lifted her large breasts under her chin and nearly choked her, sat behind the till and smiled at the room as she breathed deeply and smoked a black cigar, an eccentricity the town endured because everyone liked Momma and because she was only a Greek.

Although Georgi had been many years in Australia, he spoke with a strong accent and used Greek words and phrases when he could not remember the English. But he did not consider himself Greek. 'Georgi Comino, Australian', he would tell strangers, without taking the gold toothpick – made from the first gold he had found on the Palmer – from the left side of his mouth. The pick delighted Jamie because Georgi could twist it in his mouth and point with it. 'Hands are for talk', he would say, 'not to point.' He was so proud of his adopted country that when the *Sydney* sank the German cruiser *Emden* he took down all the mirrors on the back wall of the café – and Georgi and Momma loved mirrors painted with black and white swans flying among waterfalls – and commissioned the town signwriter to paint the battle of Cocos Island.

Jim Downes worked for weeks, even late at night, behind a canvas curtain, for Georgi would not allow anyone, except Jamie, to see what the signwriter was painting. It was to be his patriotic surprise to the town. Jamie had, a year before,

59

fought Paddy Brady under the bridge after school for twisting the arm of young Spiro Comino, a battle of bloody noses and black eyes that had lasted for more than an hour before Paddy quit, and Jamie, his shirt splashed with blood, could hardly see or stand. Georgi never forgot this defence of his son. From that day water ices dusted with sherbet and served with sweet biscuits were free to Jamie and more than repaid the skinned ear and the beautiful shiners over which Pearl wrapped poultices of hot minced liver mixed with sulphur.

As Spiro's protector, Jamie was allowed, on his way home from school, to watch Jim Downes replaster the wall and then transform it into a tropical sea with an island and bending palms on the extreme left and the outline of two battle-grey shapes that rapidly became the warships of Australian history. The *Emden* was shown, beached on the coral reef and wrecked by shellfire, her last gun still firing, the black and white cross of Kaiser Wilhelm's battle ensign still flying among the smoke and flames of defeat. And far to the right, across a white-tipped Indian Ocean with waves so still they seemed to have been fixed with glue, was H.M.A.S. *Sydney*, much bigger than she should have been at that distance, firing broadsides at the dying raider from guns that spewed orange fire and smoke half way to Cocos Island. But on the day Jim Downes climbed down from the ladder and put his brushes aside Jamie knew it was the most wonderful picture he had ever seen.

'Georgi', he screamed, 'it's finished.'

Georgi ran from the kitchen, his hands covered in flour, and stood inside the curtain, gazing at the mural almost shyly as he studied it from the white wake of the *Sydney* to the burning hulk of the *Emden*. Then he smiled and with a shout he hugged Jim Downes and kissed him on both cheeks.

'Beyootiful . . . . be-yoootiful.'

And then he did something Jamie never forgot. He stepped back, stood to attention and said, 'Brave men, Georgi salute.'

And his right hand, white with flour, came stiffly to his forehead.

Jamie never saw the unveiling, late the next night and only for grown-ups. The celebration lasted all night and even Scanlon, the Police Sergeant, was only just upright when he left the café on daylight. But for a long time the town and district talked with pride of the painting at Comino's and every stranger of note was taken to meet Georgi and to admire it.

When the pictures were out, and Comino's was closed and not even Billy Hughes could get a drink through the back door of the Royal; when the streets were empty and the earth had grown silent: Saturday night had a different personality.

Jamie would go to bed, as late as he could, and lie waiting but not knowing what he was waiting for. He would half dream of magical things that never happened. Things he could not name but was sure would happen and never did. He would lie walled by the mosquito net, unrelaxed in his pyjama trousers, aware of the night and its brooding presence. He would think of the town and its dark scrubs and the river and the sea and the mysterious south where the parrots went at the beginning of summer. He never thought of the north, not once in all those years. He envied the birds and their limitless freedom. He followed them in his mind and wondered where they went and what they saw.

And sometimes, on nights when the shadows were as silent as a burglar crossing a garden, Lobo, who slept at the end of his bed and sagged the net, would uncurl and stretch earlier than usual and, with a mutter in his black throat, would jump off without a sound and sit at the top of the back steps sweeping his tail. He was twice as big as the average tom, with green malicious eyes and his back legs were partly paralysed from an injury in a fight with a dog, so that he walked and ran with a stilted action and had a mournful double call, as if in pain, that gave him his name.

Jamie would lie waiting for Lobo's other call, a throaty wail that brought every she-cat for hundreds of yards. They came to him over the fences from the hotels, from the stables up the street, from behind the smithy where a colony lived among a tangle of broken boxes and coke and discarded shoes and rusting nails. He would meet them beyond the washhouse in the middle of the backyard where, with little wooing and hardly a caterwaul, he would mount them with terrifying ferocity. Jamie crept down one night and watched. Lobo, his tail stiff, his hair a wire brush, was surrounded by five admiring cats and not another tom in sight. One lay on her back and made inviting plays at him with a languid paw. But he ignored her and pounced on another and sank his teeth in the back of her screaming neck.

On Saturday nights like this, of waning moons floating in ash dust, stars within reach of a stick, the far smell of the sea, he could not stay in the silence. He dressed and roamed the town, wandered its emptiness, with no purpose except to explore this void and the void within himself. Wandered where his bare feet took him, within the shadows of shops and houses, disturbing dogs and hurrying on, aware of the bubbling tension inside, a need to escape into the hidden menace of overhanging trees and blackened lanes that even in daylight gave him a creepy feeling that he was being watched and hands were waiting to reach for him.

On some nights he went as far as Clay Street, past the house which the boys at school said was a knocking shop, but only once was there a light in the front room and through an inch at the bottom of the blind he saw a lady in a red dressing gown sitting at a piano playing softly to herself. While he watched she stopped and left the room and he was about to go down the path and move on when she was round from the back of the house and beside him.

'What do you want?' she said, quietly.

Jamie didn't know. Except that he wanted to run. But he could not move.

She opened the door. 'Inside.' She closed the door and jerked the blind. 'You're from the big house.'

A statement, not a question.

Jamie tried to speak but no words came.

She returned to the piano stool. They studied each other. She had a lot of hair, piled high, and her eyes were green. But soft. Not like Lobo's. And her lips were very red.

'Is anything the matter?' she asked.

He shook his head.

'Well?'

'I couldn't sleep . . . I . . . I go for walks.'

'Oh.' But not surprised. 'How old are you, Jamie?'

'How do you know . . . ?' But he didn't finish.

'I know', she said. And smiled.

'I'm thirteen.'

'You know it's bad manners to look through windows.'

Jamie felt himself shrinking. Hoped he would become so small he would disappear. Down the nearest rathole. He looked at his feet. Red with dust. He could hear his grandmother prompting. Far off.

'I beg your pardon', he whispered. 'I didn't mean . . . .'

She laughed and kissed him on the head.

'Of course you didn't.' And added: 'Your granny was kind to me. When I first came. After . . . she helped me more than I can tell. She still comes to see me sometimes.'

He knew she was about to say more but the gate clicked and boots crossed the verandah.

'You will have to go', she whispered.

A man called. Softly: 'Laura – are you there, Laura?'

'The back way', she whispered. 'You'll come to see me again. We'll keep tonight a secret, won't we?'

Jamie nodded and the door closed. He ran home and got

into bed, still feeling shame for being caught yet glad he had been caught, but thinking more about the voice muffled by the front door.

'Are you there, Laura. Are you there, Laura?'

He repeated the words to his pillow. Until something familiar about the voice came back to him. And then he knew. The bank manager, who often dropped in to talk to Grandmother. Not Mr Murdock! Surely not him. It couldn't be. His daughter was in his own form at high school. He couldn't believe it but, staring into the dark, he knew it was true.

Some nights Jamie wandered among the nameless smells of Chinatown where the shop windows were shuttered and rooms, heavy with carved black furniture, hid behind them, separated from the shops with glass bead curtains that tinkled in the breeze or made what he imagined were temple sounds when someone brushed through them. Jamie always paused at the last shop before the creek for only at night, and late, could Chee How be heard sweating sovereigns. Jamie knew this because the shop was next to the store where his school mate lived, and Chow Hing had told him, after swearing him to secrecy on a kangaroo's foot.

Grandmother still had a silver case, with slots for different size coins, but sovereigns, though still used, were scarce because of the war and were not allowed to be exported. Chee How collected them when he could from people who had hoarded them, paying a little more than the banks. When he had twenty or thirty he put them into a rice bag, tied the mouth, held both ends and poured the sovereigns left and right, backwards and forwards, in a seesaw action that rubbed off tiny shavings of gold as the coins scraped against each other. This took weeks but it was a steady part of Chee How's income. He and his family spent hours each night sweating. The flowing coins made a soft hushing that could

64

just be heard from the street if you knew what to listen for. When Chee How had sweated enough to give him a good profit, without reducing the weight of the sovereigns too much, he burnt the bag in an iron cooking dish, blew the carbon away and brushed the gold shavings into a little heap to be melted. Jamie knew that Chee How was far too cunning to change the sovereigns at the bank. They knew about sweating and weighed them on their gold scales. But Chee How had ways of sending the sovereigns and the shavings to China where high prices were paid.

Jamie roamed town on many Saturday nights until weariness overcame his restlessness, his search for something he could not explain, and eased the feeling like crumpled paper in his guts. Only then would he go home to bed, to wake long after daylight with stinking Lobo heavy across his feet, and Pearl cross because he was late again for breakfast.

But on some nights, before tiredness drove him back, he wandered the river bank where he knew every track or just sat on the rocks to listen to the water. He knew if the tide was flooding or ebbing. He did not need to see the water. He knew the struggle of the river making for the hills or its whispering slide towards the big bend and on and out to the sea where the yellow everlastings grew in mats around the base of the white lighthouse at the river's mouth.

On very still nights, when the mopokes called to each other like sad old men, he could detect the muffled clunk of rowlocks as the sharpie left the creek down river and would wait until Nosey, the old kanaka, rowed past with his nets, heading for the prawning grounds off the island upstream or the sandbar where the big whiting rested like silver fish knives in the shallows.

Or he would wait, straining for the first vibrations of the weekly goods train pounding in from the north, and hold his breath when he heard the sound, like she-oaks sighing, and hold it again as the train crossed the river and he saw the sudden flare as the fireman opened the gate and tossed in more coal.

And then the dark train, with its cowcatcher like a woman's comb, was gone, taking the hollow roar above the river with it. Heading south towards the Hungry Country and the waiting dawn until he could hear it no more although his ears still sang with the receding sound. Then at the Two Mile it loosed its whistle and the sound raced back to him across the empty night, haunting, lonely, desolate, going away, going south, going south, until even the last shudders were lost and he was alone with the river and still lonely and nothing had been resolved.

CHAPTER SIX

ON WEEKDAYS Jamie did not hear the Angelus. On Sundays it always woke him. He hated that bell, even though he turned over and went back to sleep. It rapped the town with an admonishing finger. Each rap a letter: S-U-N-D-A-Y.

The day overwhelmed him with gloom and doom and other words of foreboding. Sunday, any Sunday, poured an awful goodness into the air. Like a disease you couldn't help catching. It had nothing to do with real goodness like Grandmother or Pearl or even Mrs Jenkins who fed the old sick stockman who lived alone next door. Sunday was desolation, a word he had heard Preacher Jones use. He had found it in the dictionary between desman and despair. He liked its rolling sound but not its meaning.

Sunday was when Jamie remembered funerals and pain and brown snakes striking with the speed of lightning instead of fish hooks and ripe persimmons and silk and the whine of bicycle tyres on gravel. Sunday was when people walked more slowly and spoke in a furtive way as though afraid He would hear them and reach down from the sky with a nulla. It changed people. They laughed on Saturday nights and were glum the next morning. And some boys were not even allowed to read books about Indians or headhunters.

And the bells. Not only the cracked Angelus at the Catholic, but the other cheerless reminders of goodness. They beat out a hidden threat, a once a week chastisement for things done and things not done. There was no escape. No way of getting away from them or ignoring their solemn message. Sunday lay on the town like cane in the hollows seared black with frost. It lay on Jamie. It crept inside his head and turned his brain to suet pudding.

Sunday was the one day of the week when he wished he was a Chow with slit eyes and yellow skin. When he envied Chow Hing who, only when he felt like it and never when a bell demanded, lit a sandalwood stick and stuck it in the joss-bowl before the gold painted wood figure of Kwan Yin, with her little messenger bird perched beside her, in the corner of the room behind the bead curtain in Chinatown.

But two special Sundays stuck in Jamie's memory with the persistence of a bogged wheel in the white porous soil of the Hungry Country.

Sunday was the one day when Grandmother rose early and ordered him to clean her best shoes.

'Without any of that muck on the buckles now.'

She dressed in her best black with her best whalebone net collar and a long string of onyx beads that hung like a witch doctor's totem. She even muttered a brief grace to herself before breakfast. Jamie wanted to giggle.

Another of his Sunday chores was to lock up Admiral Beatty at half-past ten to prevent him following her to church, an act of doglike piety she disapproved. Then, fifteen minutes later and wearing her black hat, with two jet-headed pins impaling the crown and white daisies around the brim, and carrying her black parasol in one hand and in the other her hymn book with a red silk marker hanging from it like a tongue, Grandmother was at the front gate as the cab turned the corner.

'Top o' th' mornin', missus', Old Mick called from the box, touching the peak of his cap as Grandmother, with a foot on the lower iron step, and Jamie pushing from behind, emptied her frailty into the cab.

'An' a foine day tis fer th' Godfearin'.'

'Don't be a clown, Mick', she retorted. 'It's going to be a blisterer.'

'Ah, well', said Mick, picking up the reins and waiting for her to settle, 'it's all a matter of *taaa*st.'

And then he asked, as he always did, 'An' where would we be galavantin' today?'

'St Peter's Basilica, of course', Grandmother said, as Jamie slammed the low back door, with the catch that sometimes failed to grip, and she clutched the iron holding rail with a black gloved hand.

A game. Played in different ways with different lines, as Grandmother left for the dour delights of the eleven o'clock service at the Presbyterian Church where the parson, in his black gown and white bib, preached before a Burning Bush that had been painted with great care by Jim Downes. So realistically that it changed the planked back wall into a bushfire whose scarlet and yellow flames seemed about to reach the roof and consume the building.

Grandmother was at times critical of God and the Church but on 'His washing day', as she called Sunday, their misdemeanours were forgotten, their errors absolved, in the hope of storing up credit in heaven. She delivered herself, with all the eagerness of a vestal virgin, to what the Professor later called a 'corroboree of organised piety'. The hereafter was one of Grandmother's weaknesses. On week days Jamie often wondered if she gave salvation a thought.

But the day Admiral Beatty escaped Jamie waited for the dome of heaven to fall. Admiral had a personality not often given to dogs. He was pure on both sides but the breeds struggled with each other like drunks in a brawl. His sire was a pointer, his mother an Aberdeen terrier. The result: alarming. The legs of a pointer, a body too short for his legs, a small tail and a blunted head with small erect ears. Grandmother said that when other dogs saw Admiral for the first time they averted their eyes. He had the pointer colouring with stray blotches of dark grey and his longish hair had the tired look of an old sheepskin rug. Admiral, unlike his famous namesake, was a cur and had been known to run for a quarter of a mile without a glance back when a Pekinese yapped at him. He was also gun-shy. At a glimpse of Jamie's pea rifle he would dive under the nearest bed and stay there for hours making silly noises, and if he happened to be anywhere within sound when Jamie used the rifle he would fold himself into a ball, unwind like a released spring and take off howling. Over a hundred yards he was faster than a whippet, which was how he avoided the challenge of every fighting dog in town. At home his manner was warm and his habits gentle and when he curled his pointer lips over his Aberdeen teeth he wasn't snarling but giving his most ingratiating smile. He also had a passionate habit that no belting could cure. He liked horse — fresh and steaming.

This Sunday, as usual, Jamie had shut Admiral in the feed-room at the stables, where he normally complained dismally before settling down on a bag to sleep. But this day some urge only dogs understand, some race memory of hunting packs, took charge. He climbed on a box, dived through the closed window and with a short run and leap reached the top of the eight-foot fence, balanced like a tightrope walker and dropped. Once free he did not hurry. He left his visiting card on posts that deserved it, then headed for the cab rank where Emperor had only recently dropped and rolled in the smoking heap. He arrived at the Presbyterian Church just after the sermon had begun.

From the front of the church Admiral examined each row of seats, moving slowly forward and beneath them, and with every move wiping trousers and dresses as he advanced, to an accompaniment of subdued hisses, little cries of alarm and rougher dog commands. A strong ripple on the calm surface of the church, and when the ripple reached the front row a pause before it began again down the seats on the other side of the aisle.

When Admiral, seven rows down, found Grandmother he smiled and hurled himself into her lap. As she yelped and tried to push him off, helped by worshippers on either side, the parson faltered, stopped, tried to continue, lost the Good Samaritan on the road to Damascus and stopped again as the congregation became aware, for the first time as a united group in the confined space, of the overpowering sweet stench that now filled the church. At the same time worshippers were bending to examine their trousers, the hems of their skirts and even their boots and shoes and making alarming discoveries. They began to rise and hurry for the door. Twice, the parson called 'Brethren', plaintively and despairingly, for the stench had not yet reached the high pulpit below the Burning Bush and he was bewildered at the disturbance and the erratic but determined departure of his flock.

As the church emptied, Grandmother kicked Admiral down the aisle. And all the way down, cringing and resisting, he still tried to smile up at her, dog innocent of what he had done. She kicked him out of the church and down the front steps, and, never once forgetting her dignity, marched stiffly home, turning every few yards to shake her parasol and hiss, 'Filthy beast.'

Grandmother's angry homecoming was received with consternation. But as the story became clear how Admiral had emptied the church even Pearl could not keep her face straight and Jamie became so helpless with laughter that Grandmother slapped him and ordered him to his room.

From that day, under threat of terrible consequences, Jamie had to see that Admiral Beatty was shut up where he could not leap through windows, but it was still one Sunday

Jamie remembered with joy and gratitude to Admiral – and to Emperor.

But that other Sunday. That was different. In another time.

Jamie no longer went to Sunday School. He was getting older and had rebelled. He argued with his grandmother that now he was at high school he had more important things to do than listen to the prayers and texts of Angus McDonald, the superintendent, who worked in the Council. The argument continued for weeks until one Sunday Grandmother said to her grandson: 'I can't force you but I disapprove. I leave it to your conscience to guide you.'

That special Sunday, when Grandmother was sleeping off her devotions and Jamie was studying the Wars of the Roses for his end-of-year, he heard steps on the verandah and then a tap-tapping and the Professor was peering into the room like a migratory bird that had lost its way.

'Dear boy', he said, in his almost feminine voice, 'I promised you once, in a mood of foolish enthusiasm, to show you a ceremony much more beautiful and significant than the one your grandmother, bless her independent soul, attended this forenoon.'

He had been drinking but was not drunk, and seemed to be in a good mood. He had made some attempt to wipe the food stains off the faded lapels of his old tweed jacket. He even wore the remnants of a tie.

'The Boorool?'

'What else, dear boy?'

He picked up the history, read a few lines, shrugged and dropped it.

'What is history but inspired distortion? A tarnished mirror. A reflection of the opinions, the prejudices, the abuses only of the class, the party or the individual in power. I shall show you history that was never written and religion as it was before it was contaminated, transformed, and transfixed into a sideshow by prelates more concerned with trappings and with power than the majesty of God.'

He combed his thin greying hair, still stained with its original copper, with his long fingers.

'Come with me.'

Jamie had first seen the Professor some years before, when he had found him, a stranger, unconscious inside the back gate. Filthy and his clothes rags. His breathing, as he lay on his face, a rattle deep in his chest.

'Drunk', Pearl said.

But Grandmother listened more closely and shook her head.

'The man's ill – very ill.'

The doctor confirmed.

'Double pneumonia. He can't be moved.'

'Jamie. Get two men from the Royal. And hurry.'

Pearl prepared the spare room and boiled water for hot bottles. Grandmother cut off the Professor's clothes with the kitchen shears and quickly washed his face and hands and feet. Then they packed him with blankets and bottles. Jamie crept in and watched but the man's bubbling breathing scared him out. He had never heard such a sound before.

Twice in the next few days, the doctor shook his head. 'It's his heart. He can't live.'

For ten days crisis followed crisis. Then one late afternoon he opened his eyes for the first time. Sea blue and smeared with sickness but comprehending. He focused on Grandmother at the foot of the bed.

'Dear lady', he whispered and closed his eyes again.

'Oh God', Pearl said.

But when the doctor came he was more hopeful.

'I think he'll live.'

When the Professor woke next morning he was too weak to

move. But his eyes had lost the smeared look and his voice was a little stronger.

'Dear lady', he said to Grandmother. 'I appear to have made a nuisance of myself.'

'You have been ill. You must keep quiet and rest. You need nourishment.'

Pearl brought a bowl of mutton broth and together they propped and fed him.

'You are an Englishman?' Grandmother asked.

'I was an Englishman – once.'

He tried to smile and went to sleep.

The Professor recovered quickly. Soon he was able to sit in a chair. Then in the garden where he would struggle to rise when Grandmother came to talk to him.

'Sit down, man', she commanded. 'You have no strength yet for the niceties.'

He never talked about himself and one afternoon, back from a walk, in the clothes Grandmother had found for him, he carried posies of flowers wrapped in tissue paper. He handed one to Pearl and one to Grandmother.

'I found them, peering through fences, like unwanted children. For the dear ladies who saved my life.'

Every day he was stronger and soon he decided to leave. Grandmother insisted that he needed another week but he shook his head.

'But where will you go?' she asked.

She knew he had no money.

'South', he said. Vaguely. 'I have some correspondence to collect. It will correct my somewhat straitened circumstances.'

'Are you sure?'

'Absolutely, dear lady. But I shall be back. There is something in the air of this metropolis I find *sympathique*.'

He pronounced it the French way.

He left with a lunch Pearl had cut for him. In an old canvas carrying bag from the stables. And inside the lunch was an envelope with a pound note Grandmother had included. They never expected to see him again.

But months later he returned and soon the town gave him his name. Jamie saw him staggering along Boola Street and rushed home with the news.

'He was sozzled.'

Grandmother grunted. 'I suspected. I doubt if we will see him.'

He arrived a few days later. Sober but still recovering from the scatter. His hands trembled as he handed Grandmother and Pearl a small parcel each.

'Dear ladies, with my everlasting gratitude for your kindness.'

For Pearl enough silk to make a dress. For Grandmother beautiful black chamois gloves. And from his pocket a book for Jamie.

'Treasure it, dear boy, not for the history of a bloody sub-jugation, but for the sweetness of its scholarship.'

Prescott's *Conquest of Mexico*.

The Professor stayed. A craggy shambling figure about town with a nose that became more and more like a red ping pong ball. Grandmother said it must have cost him twenty thousand pounds. He was often to be found in a bar or propping a post near a bar, declaiming in his thin Pommie voice on subjects that ranged from obscure points of Roman Law to the military tactics of the Spartans. When sober for more than a few days he became sour and likely to throw a rock or a chunk of wood at anyone who came near his shanty on the western edge of town. But drunk, though not too drunk, he had what Jamie came to define in his final year as an eccentric eloquence. He never talked about himself and no-body knew positively, though the whole town claimed to know, that he had been a professor of history at Cambridge and was a remittance man, a theory strongly supported at the post office where, every three months, he collected a registered letter from England which he took, and in some haste, to the Bank of New South Wales. His affairs, once inside that institution, disappeared from public view though never from public speculation.

The Professor not only kept the town alive with his drunken arguments, but he also became the local oracle. If a scholarly though not always impartial opinion on any subject, from God to the mountains of the moon, from the campaigns of Napoleon to the Australian Aborigines, was needed to solve an argument or settle a bet, the Professor was consulted, though this could prove expensive as his capacity for whisky was immense and at least half a bottle was necessary before he would deign to answer a question or give a ruling.

On that special Sunday Jamie followed the Professor west to the end of town and into the bush. Past his shack of rusting iron sheets and cardboard and bark to a shallow stony gully a mile beyond.

'This', the Professor said, without any preamble, 'is sacred ground. More sacred than the stones of any cathedral or any temple. I hesitated before bringing you here but you are old enough, and wise enough in your youth, to know the mysteries of this place – the mysteries of a destroyed people. But never forget that in many respects their culture was more stable and more beautiful than our own. Remember, too, that the boys who became men here knew, as we are forgetting, the terror and the wonder of God.'

He snapped a black grass-tree lance and with the point traced a circle with a diameter of a dozen yards, on the hard ground.

'Here was the first sacred ring of the Boorool. And if you observe closely you will see that the outline is still preserved, as though the earth had been stained, as indeed it was by the feet of men and boys over not a few years or a few hundred years but millennia. Here was religion, stern but free of bigotry and schism. Virginal and undefiled.'

Jamie felt the trembling. Deep inside. Like an underground stream flowing through him. He could see the circle, a faint shadow on the ground, a negative, an imprint. He walked round it and faced the Professor and was aware of the change in him, a new commanding richness in his voice, a new dignity that ignored the patched clothes, the unkept hair, the stubble. He seemed older and taller and less tattered. Jamie felt the trembling fade. He waited.

'If you study the ground, as I have studied and measured it', the Professor said, 'you will observe that a pathway once led from this circle, which I call the Circle of Uneasy Sleep, along the gully. Come, I will show you.'

Jamie could not see a path. Only a faint indentation in the red earth. Little more than the earliest erosion of a seldom-used cattle pad. He followed the Professor for a hundred yards, two hundred, and still he walked. Stumbling as his worn boots slid on loose stones, his eyes to the ground, his grass-tree lance held like a war spear. Then, three hundred yards from the Circle of Uneasy Sleep, he stopped and gazed about him, as though looking for landmarks. At last he turned.

'This, dear boy, was where the main ceremonies were enacted. Look hard. You will see the Big Circle, sixty feet across. Follow me.'

Again, as they circled, Jamie could see on the earth not a track but a shadow of what had once been an immense ring in the centre of the gully. In some places, hard to distinguish, for stunted bushes had obscured it. But, again, there. A drawing in soft pencil, a line in smudged charcoal. They returned to their starting point. The Professor took off his jacket and sat on it. He drew his shirt opening together. The shirt had no buttons. He pointed.

77

'Sit, boy, and do not speak as they did not speak. Sit and learn. Understand as they did the mysteries not of a mere twenty centuries but twenty twenty centuries from the time of innocence. When the world was not yet contaminated by European men, the greatest of all destroyers.'

They sat close. Far off a curlew cried and was answered. Jamie felt that the Professor was suddenly tired, as though all the energy had drained from him. Then he seemed to have forgotten him. Jamie wondered what would happen now. Should he have come? Was he really touched as some people said? At last the Professor began to talk. Clipped words that emerged like the noses of rabbits among the stones.

'The Boorool began when the tribes for many miles around this place sent messengers with carved sticks to the nearest friendly tribes. Those tribes sent their own messengers on to the next and the next, inviting them to bring their boys and to take part in a ceremonial battle to commemorate the death of a warrior hero.'

He paused. 'They were very Greek these people. Very Greek. And in their own way they were just as great. During my reading at . . . .'

He looked at Jamie. Suspiciously. And dropped his eyes.

'As I was saying, they were very Greek. The tribes assembled here, near this Big Circle, where the boys of one tribe were handed over to the men of another for instruction in the ancient laws during the day. At night the boys – they were only a few years younger than you – slept round the Circle of Uneasy Sleep. Each boy lay on his right side with his head pillowed on the next boy's hip. In sleep the circle was complete. The circle was the balance of life. The totality of Chinese philosophy. Yes, dear boy, the yin and the yang.'

He paused, poked a little finger in one ear and vibrated it like a violin string.

'At dawn each morning the boys were kicked awake and

marched along the track to here. They were guarded by men with spears. As they marched an old man explained the meaning of the snakes and animals and emblems carved on the trees that lined the path. Round this circle – then a great clearing in the bushland and cleaned by fire – the trees were also carved and hung with phallic symbols made from plaited bark and grass. The circle itself, worn clear by feet over aeons, was marked with small clay figures of emus and kangaroos and wombats and other animals.'

The Professor grunted to his feet, rubbed a stiff knee, gave it a slap and moved to the centre of the Big Circle where he prodded for a softer patch in the stony ground and embedded his lance.

'Here stood a pole, as large and phallic as a maypole. From it hung ropes of bark, just as the streamers do on a maypole, which the old men held as they stamped and chanted. The boys were seated around the base of the pole and there they were taught the virtue of silence.'

He squinted at Jamie from beneath eyebrows as untidy as weeds and rubbed the grey redness of his hair.

'Later you will learn that wisdom begins with silence. Silence is the inner well of quiet where wisdom is born. Silence is the great genesis of thinking man. Profundity.'

He thought for a moment. 'During these days of preparation for manhood, the boys were not allowed to speak. Every subterfuge was used to make them break their silence. The casual inquiry. The sudden question. Even the command. If a boy spoke or even made a sound a guard would scatter his brains with his ironbark nulla – like custard spilt on a kitchen floor. I said earlier that these magnificent people resembled the Greeks. This is true. But they also had a discipline of the Spartans. Although the boys were fed, little and irregularly, they could not ask for food. So silence lived on the very precipice of death.'

The Professor returned to his coat and folded it a second time against the hardness of stones covered by their thin icing of earth.

'The boys spent their days here, in this circle, and were marched back at night to the Circle of Uneasy Sleep. They were taught the tribal history and laws, the meaning of the sacred stones and places, even the rules and taboos of their own bodies. And while they absorbed this history and religion and medicine, warriors circled here whirling oval pieces of wood on bark cords which screamed like women and barked like dogs. There was even one that shrieked like a circular saw.'

He pointed to the trees like sentinels above the gully. 'Beyond, perhaps half a mile away, the women heard the terrible sounds and shook with fright. To them the sounds were the voice of the great warrior who swallowed all the boys after they had been initiated and vomited them again at the end of two moons. When the ceremonies were finished, the laws taught, the food and marriage taboos explained, the sacred objects shown and reverenced and the sacred places drawn with spear points on the ground, the boys were circumcised with quartz knives – again in silence – the tribal marks were cut deep into their right shoulders and the wounds packed with clay mixed with grass seeds, and their noses were drilled with a spear point to receive the warrior bone worn only in wartime. Then, for two months, guarded night and day, the boys lived at a sacred place in the foothills until it was time for them to return.

'Now they were dressed for their emergence as men. Dingo tails were tied around their foreheads with a band of white bark above and the throttle of a snake below. An opossum robe was placed around their shoulders, crossed at front and back, with a pendant tail of opossum to the ground. Round their waists they wore belts of human hair, bands from the breast skin of wallabies went round their forearms and necklaces made from reeds were put over their heads. A streak of red ochre was painted under the curve of their noses. Two boomerangs were placed in their belts. In their left hands they carried a green bush.

'The boys were then brought back to an open square surrounded by the tribes. Each tribe sat facing the compass point of their own tribal country. Inside the square the women held yamsticks decorated with leaves. The young men, now carrying painted shields and two spears, marched into the square and circled the women who pointed their yamsticks at their kinsmen. Then, with a mass shout from the elders and to the drumming of bullroarers, the young men broke out of the square to throw spears at each other to prove their dexterity. And only then were they allowed to speak. At the first word they uttered they were warriors of their tribe. They were men.'

Jamie had listened in growing wonder at the way the Professor had filled the gully with people. Had brought to life the shadowy circles of the Boorool that were older than history. He had heard too much but still wanted desperately to hear more. And now, as the Professor stopped, his eyes closed, Jamie saw that he was asleep. He was not an old man. Not as old as Grandmother. But now he looked lined and remote, with his chin on his chest as if in prayer.

The sun was almost down and the western trees surrounding the gully fired spears across the rock littered earth. The birds had gone home and in the quiet Jamie felt he was being watched. And shivered. Not from fear but because of all those other boys, those thousands of boys over thousands of years, who had been here and who, around these circles, had left their youth behind. Jamie tried to imagine how they must have felt, half-starved, kicked into wakefulness each morning, with death waiting if they made a sound. It was like unravelling a rumour within a rumour. Unrolling and spreading

81

a strange map. He paced the Big Circle, slowly, thinking, hearing the boys breathing, feeling their dark eyes on him, seeing the clay figures, recording the whispered mysteries. He stood against the Professor's grass-tree spear, in the centre of the ring, sat where the boys had sat with clamped mouths, terrified yet proud that soon they would be men.

In the dusk he left the gully and walked back to town. He felt incredibly old and incredibly young. He thought of the dark gods behind him, the dust of time, the scream of bull-roarers, the crash of nullas, the high whistle of spears. Of when he too would be a man.

CHAPTER SEVEN

THAT SUNDAY crept silently within the sheets of Jamie's consciousness. At errant moments little pictures would spread their patterns and colours before his eyes. Sliding in from left or right as the frames did in Grandmother's stereoscope. And behind was the Professor's voice drifting across the last spears of sunlight to reach that haunted gully.

At these moments Jamie was aware, as never before, of a change in himself. Just beyond his understanding. Elusive and fleeting. Impossible to describe, except that somewhere from that Sunday, from darkly within the blood and bone of that afternoon, was a point of no return. Revealed in total silence with the passion of a lightning strike. To know and nothing more. To perceive without logic or proof. To be part of a mystery without knowledge of that mystery. Just to know in one blinding moment of irrecoverable time. To know without knowing with the impossible certainty of a bird changing its course in flight.

Yet added to that day, to the turning point on the pathway of new awareness, was a hopeless exaltation that nothing could appease. He rode his bicycle for miles along bending avenues of cane, driving at the pedals with all his weight, and returned soaked in sweat, exhausted and still as far away from a solution to the questions within his inner world as the hidden lightship far off the coast that flashed the sky on summer nights.

He told his grandmother about the Professor and the

Boorool, about the circles and the suffering boys and the silence. Everything he could remember. Breathlessly.

'I didn't understand a lot of it but I think I know what he meant.'

She nodded. Pushing her spectacles above the hook of her nose.

'I know how you feel. There are moments when only the impossible seems real. Perhaps this is why people can endure so much.' And added, after a pause, 'A clever man. But sad, unhappy. No peace there – ever.'

She was stiff and still. As she always was when thinking. He felt she would shatter if he touched her. The silence stretched, but not far enough to snap. When she spoke again she talked, he felt, to herself. To that inner woman self few men ever penetrate.

'A strange man. Tramp and courtier. A troubled soul. He never drove out his demons early enough, as most men do. They're still with him. The ghosts of his genesis. Women come to terms with their demons. They compromise. Push them away. Sweep them aside with their brooms, and with their children. They don't need reason to explain. Their bodies give them, if not the truth, then at least a light leading to it.'

She shook her iron grey head. And addressed herself again.

'But men. Men. They have no stirring bodies to whisper to them. Warnings go unheeded. So often they are silent when they should speak. They know too much and in the end know nothing. They are sires – and little else. Supreme for a moment. If they do not defeat their demons early, they are lost. As he is lost.'

Before: meaning would have surged over him like a breaker at the coast. Now: from her words, perhaps more from the way she said them, not with her mouth but from behind her eyes, as though her spirit spoke, came a trembling knowledge of what she had tried to convey, of what she had thought aloud, from the deep wells of her understanding.

The weeks drifted. Sticks going out to sea. Spinning slowly in the tide. And they did not even sight the Professor.

When he came in the back gate one afternoon he was unsteady but level in his mind. Pearl saw him from the vegetable garden and came to him. To his plasticine face, with lines like sabre cuts. She led him to the kitchen and fed him. He ate, hungrily.

'When did yer take food last?'

Watching how he cleaned the plate.

'Food . . . ah, food.'

He stirred the sugar in his tea. 'Tuesday . . . or was it Wednesday . . . Wodin . . . Thunder and war. How the god's thirst?'

'Youse a bad boy', Pearl said. Not following a word. 'Granny's under th' mango. She's bin askin'.'

He rose, holding the giddiness. 'I thank you, my blessed angel.'

And went down the path to bow deeply to Grandmother. She pointed to the canvas chair.

They listened to the leaves clapping above them and the little sounds the garden made. A cricket crossing its legs. A beetle wrapping itself in bark. A slug sliding across a rock trailing a silver pathway.

She watched him. He was the first.

'Must apologise, dear lady, for not calling before. Most remiss. A trifle, ah, preoccupied.'

'Booze.'

And followed the metallic word with a sound Jamie always thought was somewhere between a hump and a grunt. It had many meanings. Now, stern and disapproving.

'You, sir, are a highly intelligent man – and look at you.'

The words sank like stones in mud.

'I can do nothing to stop you being a sot. I won't try. But I am curious to know why you drink. To forget?'

'Never, dear lady.'

'Then why?'

'To remember.'

'And what is that supposed to mean?' Her voice rising.

He clasped his fingers on his knees. They were, like his raddled face, long and sensitive. But the nails were broken and dirty. A grave mark, a skull in miniature, crouched at the base of his right thumb.

'All those infinitesimal unfinished never started things. The what might have beens that crowd our everlasting souls. But . . . no matter. Whisky is both my mistress and my cross. I shall bear them both to Calvary.'

'Tosh', Grandmother said. Irritably. 'You're not fit for Calvary. He needed spunk to make that journey.' And added, 'His Cross was far heavier than yours. He carried it for all mankind. The Cross was not made of wood. It was an idea.'

'True, true.'

The Professor smiled wanly. The sabre cuts slashed deeper around his mouth.

'A splendid and wondrous fanatic. He knew he had found the truth. But how many have deluded themselves and the world with their own certainties? Mohammed, the epileptic. St Francis, the capricious. But I was referring to my own personal Calvary – not His.'

'You mock', she said. Sternly.

'On the contrary, dear lady. Like a clown I mock the world through myself, or perhaps myself through the world. No matter.'

She sniffed. 'Religion you reject. Yet it has always been man's harbour and his anchor.'

'Of course. To keep him in one place – tame.'

'But a safe place. We feel so much and know so little and understand less.'

He repeated her words. 'Man has only been great when he was unsafe.' He quoted: 'Safety 'tis the grave.'

'Heavens, man', Grandmother exploded. 'This instant there are several million graves in France. They weren't safe.'

The Professor nodded. 'Terrible, wasteful, foolish and magnificent. The story of history. Man is still a child, a primitive. When men stop fighting, others who do not stop will enslave them. There is no more certain lesson of history. Never forget, dear lady, that we dropped from the trees, like ripening fruit, at different times.'

They argued and sparred. Like aged puppies. He never lost his temper and his calm exasperated her. She knew that at times he goaded her. Tossing words about like mice to make her jump. In rages, she threw him out and would not see him for weeks. But he always returned. Mostly after he had been drinking. Never when he was on a scatter. Rarely when he was completely sober.

'When he's Jimmy Woodsing I can stand him', Grandmother once announced after Professor had hardly opened his mouth for an hour and left. 'But when he's on the water waggon, 'pon my soul, he's a bore.' And she added to the hollyhocks, 'I don't know why I waste my time on that creature.'

Yet when she heard he had defended her, her eyes had a new glint.

Jamie had been riding slowly past the Royal, and had dismounted to put spit on the valve of an ailing tyre, when glasses splintered inside the bar and two bodies exploding the swing doors, landed on the pavement. The first to rise was the Professor who, roaring drunk, lugged his equally drunk opponent to his feet and, with a round arm swing, knocked him into the gutter.

'And don't you dare insult a lady again you . . . you ape', the Professor shouted.

Then he slumped to the kerb and was sick over his boots – just as Scanlon turned the corner.

'At it agin', he said. Wearily.

And ran them both in. To hold them in the cells overnight.

As he marched off between them a late arrival asked what had happened.

'A bit of a blue', someone said. 'Jimmy got blotto. Called the old lady from the big house a silver-tail bitch. He didn't mean a word of it. She helped his missus last time she was sick. And the time before that.'

The Professor denied all knowledge of the fight and Grandmother was careful not to even hint that she knew she was the source of it.

'Gossip mongers', he growled. 'Nit-picking riff-raff.'

The next time they met was at the Grand Patriotic Rally in the Gardens. The day the town split into almost armed camps. And talked of little else for the rest of the week. A 'scandal' some called Grandmother's opinions at this memorable public gathering. And a few even used the word 'sedition'.

Jamie went with her to join the crowd below the bandstand. The band had already played *Tipperary* and was concluding *Three Cheers for the Red, White and Blue* when they arrived. At the last notes, in slow time for greater effect, the mill manager climbed the steps of the rotunda, called the meeting to order and announced that they would begin with the National Anthem.

The ladies composed themselves. The men took their pipes from their mouths and removed their hats. All except one. A little man with a red pumpkin face. Fred the Fettler. A troublemaker.

'Take your hat off', a man called.

Fred ignored him.

88

'Off for the King, you Bolshevik', another shouted.

'Hold this', Grandmother said to Jamie. Handing him her black bag.

She pushed through the crush and tapped Fred on the shoulder with her parasol.

'Remove your hat, sir.'

Fred turned and looked her up and down. And turned back and spat.

With a side swipe she knocked the hat off his head.

'Now will you behave yourself', she snapped.

He swung again, angrily. Took a step towards her. But the Professor was at her side, before Jamie could even move.

'Out', he said, 'until your manners mend. Or I'll be forced to . . . .'

He shambled forward.

Fred looked about for support, but the crowd began to jeer him. He picked up his hat and walked away. Muttering.

'Fighting in a public place', the Professor whispered to Grandmother. 'You're getting as disorderly as I am, dear lady.'

Later, when the 'distinguished speaker' from the south had launched the appeal, in his noted Shakespearean style, the chairman called for questions.

Grandmother raised her parasol and advanced to the steps. The crowd waited, wondering what next.

'I have a complaint, not a question', she said. 'I support the appeal but I am disheartened to hear a countryman of mine being apologetic on behalf of Australia. Talking, almost cap in hand, as though we were serfs in feudal England. Our distinguished visitor' – she snapped the words – 'referred to the mighty effort being made at home in the cause of freedom against the Hun. He ignores or forgets to mention the even mightier effort we few people have made in that same cause, and against the Boers before that. I would advise our distinguished visitor to count our crosses in France.'

She hammered the top step with the metal ferrule. 'I am an old woman. Nobody can dispute my loyalty. But I was born and reared in this country. I have only one home – here. This is mine – and yours. And the sooner people stop going on bended knee the better for all of us.'

As she gathered herself for a final effort, Jamie watched her, hardly daring to breathe. Proud but feeling conspicuous. Wanting her to stop.

'You all know me. I don't apologise for my opinions. I call a spade a spade. But I have one more thing to say. Some of the money from this appeal should go immediately to help the widows of those brave boys who have already paid the supreme sacrifice, and the boys who have had the misfortune to be maimed.'

She poked the crowd with her parasol. 'There's Tom Cash over there. Without a leg. And Tom Owen who lost an arm. And Harry Drew who has four children and can't do hard work because of the mustard in his lungs. These are the men we should help first. They fought for us. For you and me. For this country. One day, please God, every man, woman and child will be proud to say this and no other is my own native land.'

'Hear, hear', the Professor roared.

The crowd buzzed like wasps. Then some began to clap. But among the applause were calls of disagreement, mutters of disapproval.

'You're talking republicanism', a man called.

'Tosh', Grandmother snapped. 'I'm advocating patriotic humanitarian commonsense.'

The Professor reached the steps. The crowd packed closer. He was always good for a laugh.

'It is rare among human beings to hear the truth', he shouted.

The crowd stilled.

'But you have heard it today. And, having heard it, "Doubt truth to be a liar?" as Hamlet asked.'

He spread his arms like a preacher.

'You or your fathers or grandfathers came here to escape. For a multitude of reasons. Hunger. Inequality. Even persecution. You came to start a new life free from the poverty of the old. Some came because they wanted to. Others came because they had to. I was sent here too.'

He spread his arms again. 'You might as well know. You've been gossiping your empty heads off for years. I am a refugee from family and country. But all of us escaped to find a new home and this, ladies and gentlemen, is that home. Water it like a seedling. Nurture it. Watch it grow and shine and be proud. That other home is now only a dream. This is yours. It is all you have.'

He turned away and went across the Gardens. Without a glance back, even at Grandmother. All watched the tall figure in the patched coat. Stumbling. Dwindling. And some were applauding. And among the applause was cheers.

The Professor had only one male friend. Tom Plover who shared a one-room shack with the mosquitoes above the creek. Tom was older, in his late seventies, a deep-chested, moon-faced, bald old sailor who in summer wore white trousers held by a broad black belt, and a knife in a sheaf, and in winter the same trousers and a blue sweater. He had never been to school and could not read or write. He lived by hawking fish and prawns bought from Nosey the Kanaka.

One of Jamie's child memories was Tom's booming 'Fish-O' in the early morning. Tom at the kitchen steps with his Chinese basket of fresh whiting and flathead and bream and trevally neatly separated and sprinkled with nasturtium leaves. Tom filling a pint pot with the dry slither of prawns. Tom with his fishy fingers breaking off the little pumpkin shaped nasturtium pods that were hot and spicy and jumped up your nose, and chewing them because they were 'good for th' guts'.

An unusual friendship between men so far apart in background. Made possible by their nearness in generation, their intimacy of the world and Tom's knowledge of the kanaka trade. Knowledge at first hand, since he had served on a blackbirder as a young man.

Tom's Place, as it was known, was the most peaceful spot in town. In an open grove of stunted gums above the mangroves and the black mud that clicked and sucked and popped and sighed when the retreating tide exposed it to the sun. Even when Jamie was beginning to grow up he still loved it. The shack itself, held together with stray boards nailed to the sides, the iron roof so rusty and peeling that it looked diseased, the inside so clean and disciplined. A stretcher covered by a faded tartan blanket, a ship's box with brass handles, two tea chests on top of each other with scrubbed canvas tacked to them. A ship model under full sail on top of the chests, a glass case on one wall filled with shells and on another a Malay kris and a polished Brown Bess musket.

To Jamie the shack was foreign and exciting. Like Chinatown or some of the caves along the coast, or the mysterious areas of perfumed air one passed through in the scrubs. Another place. A rumour of the unknown. And if Tom was not at his Place he went to Nosey's humpy and waited there. Down the bank, just above the mangroves. Four short posts roofed with the sides of old benzine tins, overlapping so that they kept out the rain, except when there was a blow.

Here, after fishing all night, Nosey slept in the scooped earth, so that the best time to watch him at work was in the afternoon after he had wrapped his fish and bananas in banana leaves, put them on the hot stones of the earth oven and covered them with more leaves and sand. Then, while the hidden food sweated and steamed, he sat outside the humpy and carved.

Nosey was the last of the kanakas. So old even, when the new White Australia law was passed not many years before, that he had been allowed to stay when the other islanders were sent back. Too old to be dumped on any island, as many of them were, among strangers and even among people who did not speak the same language. Too old to even remember the island where he had been blackbirded.

Tom said he was a hundred years old but to Jamie Nosey had drifted, like his grandmother, beyond that.

His short white hair was a mat-like wig, his face skin and shadows, his eyes little pools of jaundiced red counter-sunk in his skull. And where his nose had been, before it was chopped off in the fight in the hold of the blackbirder's schooner when he and the others tried to escape, was a twist of scars with two holes in the middle through which he managed to breathe, except when he had a cold. Jamie was accustomed to the monstrous face, but strangers shuddered and turned away. Even Tom, who spoke a few words of his lingo, did not know where he was captured, except somewhere in the New Hebrides, where he had a Mary and four children before he was brought to Queensland and sold up-river to the big plantation.

Jamie would watch Nosey for hours as the frail beautiful fingers cut and gouged with a knife so sharp it would side split a leaf. So that the wood changed slowly and miraculously into the face of a dog or the head of a pig or the scales of a fish. But one afternoon, as Jamie squatted beside him, Nosey was carving a bigger block, working with such deftness and speed that the wood altered as he watched. Soon, two animal shapes emerged, and then he could see by the crude outline that they were pigs, one behind the other, one mounted on the other like a dog at a bitch on heat. The sow was carved with her head half turned, glancing back at the mounted boar, innocent inquiry on her face. So that when Nosey made the last shavings and scraped the wood and put down his knife and set the copulating pigs in front of him Jamie laughed. He did not realise that he had paid Nosey a great compliment but the effect was instantaneous. Nosey's mouth opened in a hideous empty grin and his whole body shuddered. Then he spoke in his own island tongue, reached for the carving and handed it to Jamie.

'You', he said.

Jamie took it home and hid it in the toolshed, under the wood in the corner that was never used, and took it out at times to admire it and feel its smooth delight. He never showed it to anyone, even his grandmother, though he knew she would let him keep it. It was his. Private and very secret. Something that linked him to Nosey and the shack along the creek and the kanakas and the islands beyond the Coral Sea for the rest of his life.

When Nosey was asleep or camping down river, Jamie liked to sit in the shade of Tom's shack. Listening to Tom and the Professor and trying to follow their endless arguments. When younger, he had imagined they were plotting some dreadful deed. Murder or piracy. He felt a conspirator. Later, he listened or if they were quiet watched the Professor cut his black plug with a penknife, if he had any money to buy tobacco, break it up with a rolling sliding motion of his palms and stuff it into his pipe. Or he studied Tom's bland face or his immense feet. Tom had never been known to wear boots and his feet, splayed and scaly, resembled those of the Komodo dragons Tom had once seen in the Dutch Indies. The nails were mortised to the flesh. The soles were blackened leather and so hard that he struck his wax vestas on them to light his pipe.

Tom would talk of sharks and devil-rays and big blows, of

the reefs he had seen up north and in the islands where the water was so clear he could see fathoms down. Of the reef near Cape York where he swore he had seen, too far down for even a Torres boy to dive, an anchor and a cannon from a Spanish galleon.

More often he would talk of the Kanaka days. The black schooners. The recruiters' boats under Spanish lugs'ls moving on a beach. Men in cabbage-tree hats and Crimean shirts with Snider carbines at the ready but out of sight.

'Them niggers. Easy at furst. Like chillun. We'd pursuade them aboard wiv trade goods, push 'em below an' slam on th' 'atches. Thems'd make a fine 'ullabaloo. They gets cunnin' after a time. When we didn't see no Marys on th' beach we knewd trouble wuz brewin'. We'd back in stern furst an' hold up th' beads an' th' turkey twill – nigs liked th' red twill – an' row back 'opin' thems'd foller us.'

Tom rolled up his right trouser leg to the long crooked scar on his calf.

'Them bastards got about us in th' shallows – off Tanna she wuz. The volcano wuz smokin' that day. Bad place – bloody bad. 'Ad ter put a volley inter'm an' club a few wiv our butts. Thems still ashore threw spears. Th' mate cops one through th' neck. Never seen so much blood. Dead as mutton. I got this. A long fish point – barbed. 'Ad ter cut 'er out.'

He shook his head, remembering the searing pain.

'Them Tanna boys – nastylike. Worse'n th' Solomon kanakas. Th' hill boys usta raid th' coast tribes an' eat 'em. Big feasts. Big 'ot stone ovens. Like Nosey's.'

Tom rolled down his trousers.

'Funny', he said. 'Still laugh ter think o' it. Them Tanna bastards usta say, "Man'o' Sydney – too salty. Man 'o' Wee Wee – very sweet". Thems wuz th' Frenchies.'

Jamie remembered, too, how they argued about the trade. Never heatedly. In a contented way as though it was history, which it was, but not remote. It had all happened only a few years before. In the time of the old Queen. And that wasn't long ago.

'A murderous traffic in human flesh', the Professor said after one of Tom's many stories. 'Slavery. In its own way as bad as anything out of Africa. Bestial, the way they were treated.'

'Thems wuz only nigs', Tom reminded him. 'There wuz some bad 'ats among us whites but most o' us shot 'em only when we 'ad ter. Sure it wuz slavery. Usta drop 'em off at th' market up river – an' on th' Mary an' th' Pioneer. Planters usta come fer miles ter buy 'em. But thems wuz only nigs, Professor. Without 'em there would've been no sugar. We should've nabbed more o' em. North o'ere ain't fit fer white folk ter work. Never will be. Kanaka boys would've made all th' difference ter this country.'

But once, when Jamie called for a pickle bottle of salted prawns for bait, Tom and the Professor were not arguing about the rights and wrongs of the blackbirder days. As Tom took threepence for the prawns, the Professor said, 'I hear she isn't very well.'

'Well', Tom repeated. 'She's gettin' somethin' awful. Scuttles around all night like a bloody sandcrab cryin' and tearing 'er clothes. Won't go ter th' sawbones.'

'But what about the girl?'

Tom squatted. His stomach bulged. To Jamie he looked like the brass Buddha at Chow Hing's. In the alcove with the long scroll and the spiralling joss.

'That bible bangin' looney'll 'ave ter take 'er. Can't 'ave 'er 'ere.'

Jamie didn't know who they were talking about. But next day, after Grandmother had returned from church, he heard her say to Pearl, 'That slut will come to a bad end. He could hardly keep his hands off her – in church.' Jamie was weeding

96

a bed outside the window, shaking the clumps and tossing them into a handcart. Her voice was loud. She talked that way when she had her head bent to take the pins out of her hat. Again he heard her say, as she put her hat into its box, 'Like a bitch on heat.'

Now the pieces came together.

Even the older boys at school called her the town bike. Enviously, since Maudie was nineteen and unattainable. When she walked along Boola Street every man letched and the older women scarified her, as they did a stranger or a new hat, with hard eyes. Even Old Mick, slumped in his cab, would wake, as if he had scented her, and trail her from under the limp peak of his cloth cap. Men would see her coming and still, as though they did not trust themselves to move, but their eyes undressed her and touched her as she passed. Or one would say 'Mornin' Maudie.' Casual and friendly, when all he wanted was to take her apart. Jackie Winn, who was married with eight children, was one of these. He kept the barber's shop where Les Darcy in black woollen fighting tights on one wall, and Carbine on another, looked down into a sleepy cave of soap and pomade and bay rum and the cheep of scissors. Jackie Winn had been known to return to a customer after sighting Maudie and snip a lump of hair that should have been left where it was. And even the chemist, who was nearly eighty and had the shakes in one hand, was once heard to mutter to his beautiful window bottles glowing with coloured water. 'She shouldn't be allowed.'

Maudie did not deliberately attract attention. She was not even a friendly girl. She rarely talked to other people and she rarely smiled. She walked from the bakery and cake shop where she worked, often with her eyes cast down, and seemed unconscious of the silent stir her progress caused. Perhaps her very passivity drew the town's attention. Maudie was not beautiful. Not even pretty. She had white skin, brown hair, small features except for a large full mouth and slanting eyes. She was tall, small breasted and long legged but her bottom was large and exquisitely rounded. The way she walked gave men dry throats and made them rattle their small change. She was never known to hurry. She walked with a gliding motion and her bottom, under her corsetless dress, rippled like a peach jelly touched with a spoon.

Jamie had known Maudie from school, though he was still only in a lower class when she reached the leaving age. He had never spoken to her – not until the trouble. When her mother was changing. He heard his grandmother say to Pearl, 'Poor soul, she's having a terrible time with the change I hear.' But he didn't know what she was changing from or into. It meant nothing at the time.

Maudie lived with her mother in a cottage out east beyond the creek. Mrs Jones, whose husband had deserted her, took in washing and made clothes. She was clever with her needle. Everyone said so. She was Tom Plover's sister, the youngest of a family of fourteen who had scattered and left the district.

She first attracted startled, then amused, attention when she appeared in clothes that were fashionable when the old Queen was on the throne. She resurrected her mother's dresses or copied some she remembered. With trains that swept the ground, long puff sleeves, even bustles. When she first appeared small boys followed her and dogs barked at the swish of her skirts. Soon grins and laughter turned to pity as people knew the reason for her eccentricity. The more charitable tried to help her, but she rejected all advances and even pushed one well-meaning lady down her front steps.

Jamie had seen her, of course. But never as intimately as the day she first performed in River Street. She stopped outside the big house and, facing the front gate, lifted her Victorian skirts and made an elaborate curtsy. This caused more hilarity, and a new wave of pity, especially when it became a ritual. Strangers were taken to watch the spectacle at ten o'clock on Tuesday mornings. But worse was to come.

As Jamie left school and climbed the stile on the side fence, Mrs Jones was waiting. She took his hand and said, 'Come on dear, we're late.' Jamie tried to free his hand but she held too firmly. He wasn't sure what to do. He couldn't push her or punch her. He felt foolish, even a little scared. And people stared and some grinned as they passed. She held his hand so tightly it hurt. He waited until they reached Boola Street opposite the Royal. Then as she paused for a dray to pass Jamie felt her grip slacken. He jerked free and ran and didn't stop until he was inside the back gate. He did not tell anyone, even Pearl. How Mrs Jones looked and how she stared down at him. Happy in a curious way or something close to happy.

The boys met him next day with bows and extravagant curtsies. They would not stop chyacking him until he had punched up a couple.

'What did the old looney say?'

'What did she want?'

All he could say was, 'I don't know.'

He wanted to forget Mrs Jones. For everyone to forget. Quickly.

That afternoon, from behind the school water tank, he saw no sign of her near the side fence. The relief was like release from the stomach ache that had recently come and gone, several times. Like sharp fingers snatching at his side. But the next day she came from a side street on the way home. She grabbed him and held him against her and through the babble he heard 'dear son'. Jamie was scared now. He tried to push her away but she held him so fiercely that he could hardly breathe and his side was like a fire. Then she relaxed her hold and tried to brush his hair. But only her face smiled. Her eyes were like the eyes of a snared possum.

99

'I've found you again', she said, and began to cry. And again he broke and ran.

In the kitchen he wanted to tell Pearl but the words would not come. They dried as they formed. Pearl would think him silly. Grownups were like that.

But Pearl had been watching.

'What's th' matter wiv yer?' she demanded. 'Like a cat on 'ot bricks.'

He shook his head. 'Nuthin'.'

'Yer bin eatin' them green rosellas agin?'

'No.' Thinking: grownups always think of your guts first.

The next day he came home another way. But she had been watching. She caught him in the lane behind the fire station near the pictures. But Maudie had been watching, too. She ran from the other end and broke them apart. She pushed her mother so hard she fell.

'Run', she snapped.

But Jamie could not move. He had never seen a woman fall before. He felt sick at the way she crumpled and lay there. All floppy and loose. He thought she was dead.

Maudie began to cry. An angry crying as she helped her mother up.

'He's not your baby', she said.

So fiercely that the words slashed the air.

'Come home. Mum. Please come home.'

Jamie ran back and into the kitchen. The words poured like Maudie's tears. Pearl pushed him into a chair.

'What's a'goin' on, yer young devil?'

Jamie told her. And then, desperately: 'She thinks I'm her son.'

Pearl poured him a glass of lemon juice.

'I knew'd somethin' wuz up.'

After that it was grownup business. Scanlon talked to his grandmother. Pearl told him. And the doctor talked to his grandmother. And Jamie did not know any more for what seemed a long time. So many things happened.

During school holidays at the coast the hot stabbing pain started again. Only this time there were fishhooks in it. It was still there in the morning and in the afternoon. His grandmother tried to telephone the doctor and Joe Speight at the bicycle shop who drove for her. But the telephone from the coast was full of whistles. So Jamie was put in the back of the Ford, with an eiderdown under him, and they started for town. As it was an emergency the storekeeper's son drove the car.

Jamie never forgot that evening. Sad and peaceful and beautiful. Cloudless and so clear that the mountains inland were a ruled line of Reckitt's blue. At every bump his stomach stabbed and he felt sick. Then a back tyre punctured and for what seemed hours he listened to the driver cursing as he jacked up the car and heaved with the steel levers to get the tyre off the rim. Then he had to put a patch on the horseshoe nail-hole in the tube and sit on the patch for half an hour until it stuck and the tube could be stuffed back and the tyre heaved on to the rim. The pump, rocking up and down, made a pleasant wet sucking.

From where he lay as they went on he could see part of the steering wheel and the little lever that advanced the spark. His grandmother, with a scarf over her motoring hat, sat beside the driver and every now and then she would turn and say, 'It won't be long now.'

They were still some distance from town, with the cane fields flowing like seawater for miles on either side, when the sky, darkening but still pale, filled with flying foxes until there was hardly space between their wings. Jamie watched them and forgot the pain and even above the engine and the wind he could hear their pulsing hush as though they were all whispering. Thousands of the great bats filled his eyes, heading inland from the down-river scrubs, and as the sky changed, blue to dark blue to grey to night, he could still see their movement by the flickering of the stars between them.

Jamie was still immersed in the peace of that evening when he was carried in and his clothes replaced with thick hospital pyjamas that itched. His grandmother bent over him and her eyes were troubled and she was gone. The Matron, in a long gown that made her taller and wider, slipped her arms under him. Her face swayed with the sudden pain and he was stretched on a long white high table. He saw cracks like a spider in its web on the ceiling. Faces were upside down and a hand hovered over him. A bird's claw. Then a white cup came from nowhere to cover his face and a sickly sweet smell smothered him. He screamed and struggled but weights sat on his arms and legs. He felt he would burst. His screams were splashed with orange and blood and stars exploding as he fell backwards into a scrabbling pit full of snarling flying foxes.

A few weeks after his appendix came out, just before it burst, Jamie was watching Tom Plover mend a prawn net for Nosey when the Professor came down the path and cautiously let himself on to the grass. His thin face was swollen. The cork of a whisky bottle peered from his coat pocket.

He stared vacantly at Jamie. 'Appendectomy . . . heard you . . . you were sick . . . now you've joined old King Eddie . . . he was first . . . to have the operation.'

His chin dropped and he slept as Tom fed the bone shuttle through the fine mesh and a flight of black shags streamed up river. He slept for the time Tom took to mend the hole and discover another. Then he opened his eyes.

'And what is the latest bulletin, Plover?'

His voice was clear, precise. He no longer even looked tired.

'Bin put away', Tom said. He did not look up.

'When did you hear?'

'Scanlon . . . few days back.'

The Professor scratched. 'Poor Emma.'

Tom grunted. 'Me mother – all over agin.'

Jamie knew then that something awful had happened to Mrs Jones.

CHAPTER EIGHT

WHEN EMMA JONES was taken south, in the locked mail compartment of the weekly goods train, Maudie went to live with Abraham Jones, her father's eldest brother. Reluctantly, since she did not like her uncle. But as Tom Plover could not take her, she had nowhere else to go.

Abraham Jones owned a farm on the road to the coast. A landmark in the district for above the front gate was a large sign, repainted many times, in Old English lettering, 'Prepare to meet thy God. Thou wilt be born again.' Abraham had painted the sign himself. Decades before when the family had first come to the district. He had been born in England. That was known. And had lived in the United States. He knew by heart some of Lincoln's speeches. Beyond that his history was a mystery. Even Maudie knew practically nothing about the family.

He was a gaunt pole with long powerful arms and a face chopped into deep lines. They resembled scars that had never healed properly. His long unbrushed hair was the grey that has been too long in the sun and wind and has gone rusty. But his eyes, deep brown and staring, were noticed most. They surveyed the world with arrogance and condemnation. A tortured face. Stained with suffering.

During the week Abraham, or Preacher Jones as he was commonly called, worked his farm with grim efficiency. His furrows were straight, his cane was clean, not a fence or a gate needed new posts nor the wire stretching. And early every Saturday he drove the short distance into town in his green spring cart, loaded his supplies and drove back again, with hardly a word to his fellow citizens. But late in the afternoon he returned, wearing his long preacher's coat, green with age, and a soft white collar and black string tie. He pulled in beside the smithy in River Street, took the horse out, swung a nosebag over its head and tied it loosely to the hitching post before striding towards his corner – Preacher's Corner as it was called – across the road from Comino's café. There he set up his home-made portable lectern under the corner gas lamp and on it placed his stained leather-bound Bible.

For an hour he preached in a voice that could be heard a block away. A booming sermon on sin, repentance, the bottomless pit, the end of the world. Pausing at intervals to open his Bible at places marked with turkey feathers and to shout long passages against the gathering noise of Saturday night. Winter and summer he was on Preacher's Corner and had been there for as long as most people remembered.

He did not mind if two or twenty listened or if his words bounced unheard on the pavement. He talked with shuddering conviction, with an ecstasy that seemed to come from an inebriation of the spirit, as though the biblical words and phrases, his warnings of damnation and hellfire for the wicked, had taken command of him and he spoke in tongues.

He would stop in mid-sentence and gaze so long at his listeners that they became restless in the transfixed silence. Then, as if he had been waiting for new words to gather in his mouth, his sermon on sin or the devil would explode again and his words would stumble over each other before meaning returned and order was restored.

The larrikins avoided him. They loitered on the other side of the street. They had clashed with him and showed no desire to repeat the experience. Two had jeered one night.

With a bound he had gathered them by the collars of their bum freezer coats and banged their heads together. And another time, after a clash, four lay semi-conscious in the gutter.

But the larrikins were not the only ones who feared him.

Jamie, too, avoided Preacher Jones until he was much older. Hurrying back from an errand in Chinatown, clutching a parcel in one hand and the change in the other, he stopped to listen to the passionate words and laughed because, in his long coat and with his arms outstretched, the Preacher looked just like a scarecrow he had seen on one of the farms.

Preacher Jones stretched out, lifted him by his belt and, dangling him off the ground, shouted, 'Devil's spawn. Get thee to thy home and learn repentance through holy prayer.'

He didn't drop him. He put him down almost gently and continued his sermon. Jamie reached home red in the face, blown and still shaking, but he didn't tell what had happened. He said he had been practising running. He knew that if he told, his grandmother would be angry and go to Preacher Jones and learn the facts. He would never be able to explain that the Preacher looked like a scarecrow. Grownups would never understand. They did not laugh at scarecrows. But for a long time Jamie scuttled into a shop or crossed the road if he saw the Preacher coming.

Preacher Jones and the Professor were flint and steel. They did not clash often. But some nights, after the hotels closed, the Professor would head for the Corner, as though driven by some demon, to attack the Preacher for his bigotry, to dispute the sacredness of holy writ, to argue the meaning of a word. Never the same, and the Professor's behaviour and his words depended entirely on the amount of whisky he had inside him.

'The Devil lurks around every corner', the Preacher shouted one evening. 'You who are heavy with sin do not recognise his evil presence. He takes all shapes and forms. He can be a dog or a horse, or a man.'

He glared at the Professor. He had seen him coming.

The Professor swayed like a branch in a strong nor'easter. He was so crumpled and filthy that he could have spent the previous night along the river bank, and probably had. But he was steamed for a fight.

'What unmitigated balderdash you talk', the Professor shouted back. 'You make God and religion hideous with your mouthings. Christ the gentle saviour. Religion the tolerant way. You make Him a monster and religion an obscenity. The Inquisition still exists – in minds such as yours.'

'You scoff. You blaspheme. You, who spend your days and nights in debauch. A shameful example to the young.'

'Yes, you old billy goat, I scoff. But I do not blaspheme. I have no religion myself, although I have tolerance for the faithful. But none for medieval fanatics.'

The Professor took a firmer grip of the lamppost.

'Man is not good and he is not evil. He is both. That is what makes him man. Able to think. Able to create. Can you imagine a genius like Shakespeare being all good? He probably had filthy habits – like me. And have you ever thought, preacher of doom, that the God of gentle people who have faith and your Devil may be indivisible?'

'Hark, brethren, to the mocker', the Preacher screamed, so that people up the street turned to listen. 'The thunderbolts will strike him. He will feel the wrath of God.'

'When all know beauty to be beautiful, then ugliness exists', the Professor shouted back.

He was beginning to enjoy himself.

'When all know goodness to be good, then evil exists. A great Chinese thinker said that. If God exists, then the Devil must also exist. Perhaps it is we who have created the one the better to understand the other. How can we know good without also having evil to make good understandable. You do not want to drive out the Devil, Preacher, because if the

Devil does not exist then God is a meaningless word. The Devil, Preacher, is as necessary to you as food and drink. If you take away God or the Devil, then your religion ceases and all your mouthings will fall on barren ground.'

Preacher Jones grabbed the Bible from the lectern and, raising it above his head, advanced.

'I will smite thee, Satan, even with the holy book of God. I will . . . .'

'Abraham.'

The name a command. From the back of the crowd that had gathered.

'Put that down.'

Big Scanlon reached the lectern.

'Enough for one night, I think. You, Professor. Home, or I'll run ye in I will. And you, Abraham. It's five minutes I'll give ye to git out o'town.'

'We were just having a friendly metaphysical disputation', the Professor said. Loftily.

'So I heard', the Sergeant said. 'An' the holy book about to be used as a blunt instrument. Out . . . both of ye. Or I'll put ye in the cells – together.'

Once a year Preacher Jones went on what Jamie's grandmother called a retreat. It had nothing to do with soldiers or battles, so that it sounded silly to Jamie. The Preacher went to the coast and lived in a cave among the rocks on the long point, below where the breadfruit trees crouched like brown spiders. He lived on bread and water and slept on a blanket. And every afternoon, when the waves raced along the reef like brumbies with white manes and streaming tails crashing to death on the black rocks, he preached to the sea. Watched by silent people or people who argued that he was crazy, he stood alone and lonely against the spray that hung like white lace against the troubled water. A battle, a bitter conflict, without victor or vanquished, as the winds snatched words like God and damnation and tossed them away and returned to stream his wild grey hair.

During one of these retreats, when Preacher's Corner was vacant for a fortnight, and not long after Maudie had gone to live at the farm, she took Bill Purdy, who was seventeen and worked at the smithy, to the barn loft behind the farmhouse and seduced him on a heap of sacks laid on a pile of unhusked corncobs kept for pig feed. But the Preacher's housekeeper, an ancient cousin on Emma's side, whose eyesight was failing but who could hear a mouse move three rooms away, heard the scrabbling in the loft and told the Preacher when he returned, exhausted and nearly a stone lighter.

When Maudie came from work he tied her hands to the separator in the dairy and thrashed her with a riding crop. Then he went on his knees and called to God to forgive her sin. As he prayed he put a hand on her knee. She waited her chance and laid him out with a kick on the jaw.

In that first year every time Abraham Jones reached for the crop her resistance stiffened. When she was sixteen, she told him that if he hit her again she would go to Sergeant Scanlon. In turn, the Preacher threatened to report her, as her guardian, as uncontrollable. They had reached stalemate. From that time his preaching became more violent and his retreats, when he allowed himself only a small piece of stale bread and one cup of water a day, more masochistic. And Maudie in what seemed to be an endless search, hunted the town.

She would never allow herself to be approached. She rejected any man who tried. She selected and ran to earth. But the violent couplings never endured. A few weeks. Seldom more. Even as they were wilting she chose another, and another. The pips lay all over town where she had spat them out. The youngsters first. Then she began to hunt among more mature trees. She never hurried. She was never conspicuous.

Then, in the Gardens, she selected Angus McDonald and, from a seat on the slopes below the bandstand, watched with a new and dedicated purpose. As superintendent, Angus was rehearsing his Sunday School girls in a maypole dance for the Presbyterian fête, positioning them so that as they sang and circled the red white and blue streamers plaited the pole and the girls finished in a cluster at its base. Maudie watched the pole, thick as a caber and fifteen feet high, and she watched Angus, a good looking bachelor of twenty-four with light brown curly hair and an earnest expression behind his glasses. A man who took maypole dancing as seriously as his job on the Council.

For once the conquest was not easy. Angus was a simple man with strong beliefs and firm opinions about the behaviour and place of women and the sinfulness of sex outside the marriage bed. He was aware of Maudie and her reputation but regarded gossip as un-Christian and gave her the benefit of the doubt.

He noticed her, however, with new interest when she began to attend morning service, particularly as he knew that Preacher Jones riled against all churches because Christ had spoken to his followers in the open and had no synagogues like the Jews, no temples like the Romans. What Angus did not know until later was that Maudie had defied her guardian in even entering the Presbyterian Church.

'You defile yourself', Preacher Jones had stormed. 'You spit on Christ, who wanted nothing of churches and images.'

'I'm going', Maudie had said.

Angus was polite but shy when Maudie bumped into him in the church doorway. It made her more determined. She ignored other men and redoubled her efforts. By going to morning church, by sitting first near him and then one day beside him and the next Sunday in another seat, she saw how more and more his eyes followed her. Soon he was waiting for her to arrive, for her smile, the flicker of her fingers on his arm, the smell of her body that made him lose his place in the hymn book. Only when she knew that his hands tight clasped on his knees wanted to search for her, did she suggest a picnic.

They went early, in his white sharpie, to catch the flood tide. Upriver through the now-smooth rapids to the point where the stream narrowed and broke into deep white sand pools overhung with wild pepper trees. Few people from the town ever went so far. They were alone with the river and the pelicans. Angus made a fire and cooked a late breakfast of eggs in the blackened pan and boiled a billy. They ate and talked. Angus talked about himself and his job and the farm he wanted to lease. He had never been able to talk freely to anyone before, especially a woman. Nobody had ever listened. Except Maudie.

Later, as the heat gathered against the river and a colony of cockatoos whitened a tree, Maudie took off her clothes and dived into the nearest pool and with a stumbling rush he followed her, and when they had kissed and splashed and played, she lay on the tent fly on the sand under the pepper trees and pulled him down to her.

To Maudie's astonishment, they continued to meet and lie together, into the months. She had no urge to break with him, as she had broken with the others. For the first time she was satisfied and secure, as though he was father and mother and husband and child all made in one. She could talk to him and he would listen, and understand. About her mother. About Abraham. Other men. Until one night as they lay together, she looked deep into him in the half light of his room.

'Angus. I never said this to another man. I love you.'

And Angus kissed her breasts and said, 'This sinfulness must stop. We will marry next year. It is God's will.'

'But what about him. He doesn't know about us?'

'I'll tell him.'

'But he even tried to stop me.'

'He won't stop us getting married.'

'He might try. I'm not twenty-one.'

'We'll see', Angus said.

'But he's acting strange – more than usual.'

She clutched Angus. 'Don't go. I'm afraid.'

On his next half-holiday, Angus slipped on his bicycle clips and rode out to the farm. Over the creek bridge and between the cottages and shanties of the East End to where the road to the coast became a red track between the cane.

As he pedalled he thought of Maudie and how he would approach the Preacher. He would tell him they intended to marry as soon as he had enough money saved to give up his job and lease the farm up river. If he refused his permission until she was of age, they could go south and find someone to marry them there. The words kept time with the pedals, with the singing tyres, with his breathing. He smiled at how worried she had been.

Angus believed in God in a deep personal way, but the arched warning over the entrance to the Preacher's farm made him uneasy. He did not even glance at the words as he passed under them. He knew them. They brought God uncomfortably close, made Him too much a threat. He conceived God as a kindly old man with white hair, not a bearded, twisted face threatening thunderbolts from the sky. Not eyes glaring down at him and everything he did. And knowing his every thought. That was the old God, not of the Bible, but what men had made of him in times since.

He rode along the drive between the mango trees to the

back of the farmhouse where the old housekeeper was feeding the fowls.

''Eard yer bike', she said, peering with declining eyes. 'What yer want?'

'The Preacher', Angus said. He propped his bike against the fowl wire. 'I'm Angus . . . Angus McDonald.'

''Eard that Maudie speak of yer.'

'Is the Preacher about?'

'Don't like folks comin' 'ere.' She came up to him. ''E don't like it. Down the back paddock. You take care. Got 'is gun.'

'His gun . . . there's nothing to shoot around here.'

She turned and went towards the house.

'Warned yer', she called, without looking back.

Angus shrugged. A bit cracked. Maudie had said so. He skirted the barn and went along the cow pad to the big field where the cane had been left to ratoon. It was high and thick and the trash and leaves made a dry clashing. He had almost reached the far corner when the Preacher stepped from the cane.

'What are thee doing on my land?'

'I want to talk to you, Preacher. I'm Angus McDonald.'

'I know thee. You're trespassing.'

Angus shook his head. 'I have something to ask you.'

Despite his grey flannel, working trousers, heavy boots and wide black hat, the Preacher still looked to Angus like an elder in an illustrated Bible he had at home.

'It's about Maudie and me.' He hesitated. 'We want to get married . . . next year. You're her guardian. We'd like your permission.'

At Maudie's name the Preacher had stiffened. He came slowly up to Angus.

'Out', he shouted. 'Fornicator . . . son and daughter of Satan . . . . Out!'

And, before Angus could defend himself, he crashed his fist into his face.

The blow knocked Angus off his feet. As he scrambled to rise the Preacher grabbed a stick and belaboured him. Angus rolled and got to his feet but a glancing blow on the head staggered him. But he managed to evade more blows and stumbled out of range. The Preacher did not follow.

'A curse on thee, fornicator', the Preacher shouted. 'May God's fire smite thee. May the . . . .'

Angus hesitated, then walked slowly back to his bicycle. He wiped his nose with the back of his hand and saw the blood. There was blood on his shirt. He was still trembling. He realised there was nothing more he could do.

In the yard the old housekeeper came up to him.

'Told yer.'

And as he rode out of the yard she called again but the words lost themselves among the mango leaves.

At the police station the Sergeant slowly shook his head.

'Sure an' you could bring a charge. An' what would the Preacher say? I tink he'd say you came on to his farm, widout his consent, to cause trouble. Because of Maudie. An' what did he do? He ordered you off an' you attacked him.'

'But the man's a screw loose', Angus protested.

'Touched on his faith to be sure. A difficult man he is. Leave it be, me boy. It's a quiet word I'll be having with him.'

'But what about the gun? The old woman warned me.'

'Did ye see the gun? No. Did he take a gun to ye. No.'

Scanlon hoisted his heavy body. His chair squeaked with relief.

'It's a touch of the fairies the old woman has. In the family it is. Beggin' yer pardon o' Maudie.'

Angus told her – and only her. But Scanlon told his constable who mentioned it to a friend. And the old housekeeper told a neighbour. Soon the town knew of the fight at the farm. And soon there were so many versions that few knew what had happened. Jamie heard three stories from his school mates but by then the fight had almost been forgotten.

When Jamie thought of that last year, and tried to recall all that had happened and when, he returned to one starting point. Not the fight but the dog plague that followed. Even men who had wandered from Cape York to the Corner could not recall such an event before, though some of them knew of starving dingoes gathering near water in drought times in the back country and hunting in small packs. Old bushmen could hardly believe what their eyes told them.

The dogs came in from the north-west, from over the mountains where no rain had fallen for three years. In the beginning, in ones and twos, then in small groups, running with heads down as if on a strong scent. They were hardly noticed at first. People remarked the strays around town and forgot them. But as the dog flow continued, as if driven by some unendurable pressure, they merged into packs and each pack seemed to have a leader. Mongrels most of them, with here and there dogs with the golden hair and darker leg markings that showed dingo strain. They were all thin and hungry and nervous from long hunger. Unnaturally alert. A bad sign. The packs spent the days along the river bank but at night they jumped fences and dug under them to raid the tins of pig feed left outside for farmers or the cut-down water tanks in most backyards where kitchen rubbish was left in the sun to dry for burning. Or the packs lay in the streets after a hunt, snarling at anyone who came near them, and even advancing with tight hair and curled lips.

No domestic dog or cat was safe and Jamie never forgot when Fred, the old cattle dog from the Royal yard, got out and trotted towards a pack in River Street. Fred joined them, innocently, sniffing, and disappeared in a catastrophe of struggling bodies, terrible sounds of torn calico, and muffled squeals and bloody yelps. In minutes nothing was left. They ate his bones, his skull. Even his leather collar. The only echo of Fred was the mark of their tongues on the street where they licked the few splashes of blood. To Jamie there was no horror in Fred's disintegration. It was too unexpectedly violent and quick. Violence taken into another time. A chilling unbelievable feeling inside. Fred might never have existed.

Only a little later, as he watched the pack, some of them sleeping in the dust, he felt the cold rising from his guts. Glacial. As the delayed horror at what he had seen wrapped him like a wet sail. He could no longer watch. He sat under the mango tree, very still, listening to the leaves, until the feeling faded and soaked into the ground and left him, and he was free again from those awful moments.

But that afternoon a girl was attacked by a small pack in a side street and was saved by a horseman who spurred into them. And a man was savaged on both legs as he left his back gate. Only then did the town become fully aware of the danger, since most of the dogs stayed near the river by day and within range of the horse-troughs in the centre of the town and seldom moved except as loners into other areas.

There was talk of omens. Of a visitation. Children were kept from school. People stayed inside their homes at night listening to the chill howling or the panting rustle of the packs hunting the streets or the frenzied scratching for the food smell at back doors by dogs that had jumped fences or got under them. People were afraid to use their backyard dunnies at night unless other members of the family stood guard, and Dan refused to change the tins unless he had protection on his rounds in his black stinking cart.

Then the shooting began. Jamie was the first when three dogs came up from the river in daylight and nearly caught

Pearl returning from the vegetable garden. He shot one from a window with his pea rifle, then climbed the mango tree, which gave him a wider field, and shot the other two. But spent and ricochetting bullets became more dangerous than the dogs. Windows were broken and bullets and pellets thudded into wooden walls. Then a .32 cracked past Scanlon's head in upper Boola Street, and through the sitting room of a cottage three hundred yards away.

The Sergeant, after talking to the Town Clerk, called the night girl at the exchange and asked her to tell the half dozen subscribers he gave her that a public meeting would be held next morning outside the Council Chambers. He also sent his Constable by bicycle to people who did not have the telephone.

But the men had only just gathered when Preacher Jones arrived in his spring cart, tied his inside wheel and advanced towards them. He wore leather leggings and carried his double-barrel shotgun under his arm.

'Halt, brethren', he called, as he approached. 'The solution is in my hands.' He grounded the butt. 'All night I have prayed for guidance and my prayers have been rewarded. Now I bring thee the word. The dogs are a visitation from the Lord for the sins of this town. For the lechery and drunkenness about us.'

'That's as maybe', someone said, 'but the concern of this meeting is how to get rid of the packs.'

'The Lord has commanded me to destroy them', the Preacher retorted. 'His work is done. Mine is about to begin.'

'But you're only one', another protested. 'We've been thinking of poison or rifle groups – three or four men each.'

'There is no need', the Preacher said. 'The Lord has directed me. If you will give me the shells I am ready to begin His cleansing work.'

Some supported the Preacher. Others thought that groups of riflemen would be better. Others still felt that the groups could be dangerous unless their movement about town was properly organised and controlled. They all looked at Scanlon.

'I tink you'll agree there's been too much shootin' already', he said. 'A bullet nearly clipped my ear. I tink it would be best to let the Preacher be. It's a good shot he is and the good Lord'll probably make his aim better.'

A few laughed but stopped as the Preacher went on his knees and began to pray. The men waited. Avoiding eyes. Then he stood, broke the gun and loaded the red cartridges.

'I shall start along the river. Bring me more shells there.'

He snapped the gun and strode off.

All that day and deep into the night the Preacher's gunshots echoed over the river. He found one large pack asleep and emptied his barrels into them. He picked them off in groups and singly. Sometimes he sat and cleaned his hot gun, waiting for them to settle, before he attacked again. He was back next day and that night, and the next. The intervals between the gunshots lengthened. And at last the choking yelps of dying dogs ceased.

The Council cart picked up forty bodies along the river and there were still dead and dying dogs all over town. The maimed that had escaped the Preacher were shot or knocked on the head. By the third day the packs had been slaughtered and the remnants had scattered. A few small groups, no more than two or three together, were seen on the southern road and crossing fields, all moving south, running limp-tongued with their eyes on the ground.

That Saturday night the Preacher, gaunt and red-eyed, was clapped on his Corner opposite Comino's. He ignored the applause and for an hour delivered a wild sermon that echoed, like his gunshots, against the shops in Boola Street. His audience could not follow what he said, but they knew the hidden words were directed at them.

CHAPTER NINE

ONE of Jamie's jobs was to raise the Australian flag over
River Street every Anniversary Day. Although the only flag
in the town that day, except at school, his grandmother
insisted that he put it up. It was a ritual that went back to her
childhood. Across the vast paddock of her history she still
remembered a march of redcoats in George Street when, as a
small girl on a visit to Sydney, and the colony not yet sixty
years old, she had watched a birthday parade. This passionate
feeling for her past, and especially her origins along the
Murrumbidgee, was a strange slow fire, fed through the
nineteenth century and burning stronger now than ever
before.

But to Queenslanders Sydney, New South Wales, was
almost another country. So far away and so divorced from
the north, for most of the long span since the first convicts
were sent up the Brisbane River, that to most people it was
foreign. Sydney was the wicked city with strange goings on. To
see once in a lifetime if you could afford the fare. On a honey-
moon perhaps. And Melbourne was too far away to even
think about and Adelaide and Perth in other countries. Life
in those places and what had happened there in the dim past,
with no associations and few family links, meant little a
thousand miles and more north, and less another thousand.
And so the town, except for rare individuals, seldom gave
January 26 a second thought. The flag in River Street was
merely another of Grandmother's eccentricities and so was

her choice of flag. She refused to fly the Union Jack. She said it was not her flag. And that was that.

In Jamie's last year, however, on the third anniversary of Gallipoli, and for the first time, she took the flag from the hall cupboard and pushed it at him.

'It's Jack's day', she said. 'It's time we honoured those boys. Half mast – and not too high.'

She always called it Jack's day. After a great-nephew who had been killed at the landing. Just as he reached the beach. A Turkish bullet in the centre of his forehead. So that all he ever knew of Gallipoli was the shallows of the cove crashing up to meet him.

Jamie put the flag up and tied the cords. Grandmother nodded approval.

'It may help remind a few that this is the only day they can call their very own. If I had my wish I'd close the town, the hotels first, and send everyone to church. Not to pray. That's for the Lord. But to feel proud.'

Jamie still remembered, and the fierce sad way she spoke, and the impact of the words, when he woke after Anzac. And suddenly he was thinking of the war, as he had never thought about it before, and it was closer. An angry gust from a virgin sky.

He lay under the net trying to recall what, until this moment, the war had meant to him. Fragments. Like shrapnel. Words. Pictures. Reports in the paper that made little sense. Words like 'offensive' and 'captured ground' and 'objective'. Foreign names. Ypres, Somme, Paschendale, Vimy Ridge, Tannenburg, Beersheba. Always foreign in an atlas of far places, and meaningless. Flags. The flags of the nations in a magazine. And pictures of trenches and torn trees. A paddock of ringbarked trees in the bright moonlight. Perhaps the moon looked like that, but nobody would ever know. Coloured silk cigarette cards of dreadnoughts and U-boats. From packets of De Reszke and Players and from Capstan Navy Cut tobacco. He had a box full of them. So many that he swapped for a set of Armada galleons. The *Santa Maria*, the *Santiago* and others. And aeroplanes. Cards of Taubs and Camels and Spads and Albatross. Another scrapbook. More aeroplanes. Even a Handley-Page, the 'Bomb Berlin Bus'. His grandmother in the drawing room, holding a yellow telegram that seemed to burn her fingers. Not Jack. Tears for another, younger, only eighteen. Died of wounds the impersonal print said. Where? How? It didn't say. The German raider off the coast. The rumour that was never more than a rumour. And that reminded him of the *Emden*. And pictures of the Kaiser in his Prussian helmet surrounded by Death Head Hussars. And Hindenburg and someone called Ludendorff. Wounded soldiers about town. One with no legs who pushed himself in a little cart. Black casualty lists in the paper. Day after day. Names that meant nothing. Killed names. Wounded names. Just names. Words again. Like 'shell shock', 'over the top', 'fire step', 'drumfire', 'shell holes', 'bullybeef', 'whizbangs', 'no-man's land'. Words far away and dreamlike. Like lessons at school about kings and queens and capes he would never see and could hardly believe existed. Except between the pages of ink-stained books or in an atlas scaled at one inch to every five hundred miles.

He pulled back the net and got out of bed. Still thinking. The young man in khaki in Boola Street only a day or two before. He didn't recognise him until he waved from Old Mick's cab. Heading for the railway station. He looked so different and grown up. A wave and he was gone. Un-remembered and remembered and lost in seconds. A centimetre in time. One of the big blokes. Three, no, two years ahead of him at school. Only two years.

Dimly now he felt the war as a presence. A gathering mass.

Just mounting the horizon. Something that was no longer happening in another place to other people at another time. But rushing at him. Like the fireballs that danced and hovered with floating menace over the summer fields before a dry electric storm.

In a few months he would be seventeen. Apprehensive but not afraid. Fear was another thing. Falling into the river before he could swim. Out of control at the bottom of the long steep hill on the coast road. Fear was not guns you had never seen except in pictures throwing shells you had never heard exploding on foreign earth. Shells from heavy howitzers on the Western Front. Big Bertha pointing at Paris. More names. More enigmas.

But the war was violently closer. No longer remote, like the long-forgotten boys around the Professor's Boorool circles beyond the edge of town. It was here, now, this moment. Himself as he cleaned his teeth. Three letters of fire above the mountains, rising from the sea. The word crunched like thunder over him and rolled on and, growling, returned.

Soon he too would have to go. To join so many others. He knew not with dread but with a hidden excitement, all messed up with the picture of a legless man in Boola Street with a black patch over one eye. The same feeling, only different, when he wondered sometimes what would happen if he stopped breathing.

CHAPTER TEN

FEW NOTICED one Saturday that the Preacher was absent from his corner. And fewer would have cared. He could be on another retreat. Anywhere. Even the baker was not concerned when Maudie did not come to work. It had happened before. When he saw Angus McDonald outside the post office he casually mentioned that she was probably sick, but Angus, back from an inspection and aching after thirty miles in the saddle, decided to go to the farm next day if she did not report for work.

But the farm was deserted. He knocked at the house and, remembering his last reception by the Preacher, cautiously searched the barn and the dairy and the inner fields. He returned and tried the back door. Locked. Worried, he pedalled back to town and round to the police station.

'Maudie never mentioned goin' away?' the Sergeant asked.

'Not a word.'

'Fishy. I tink I'd better take a look.'

He was about to get his bike when his constable hurried up the path.

'Ran into old Hughes – near the Preacher's. Said he'd heard a shot over that way. Didn't take much notice until the Preacher's dog limped into his yard – with its hide full of pellets. Said he was going to let you know, but the wife took sick.'

'Gettin' fishier', Scanlon said, And to the constable, 'You stay.' And to Angus, 'I tink you'd better come wid me.'

They beat on the farmhouse door and searched the out-
buildings. They returned and rattled the windows.

'There's only one ting to do', the Sergeant said at last.

He shouldered the back door and broke the lock. The old
housekeeper was on the kitchen floor. Her eyes were open,
her mouth slack and twisted.

Scanlon felt her pulse. 'Looks like a paralytic the poor old
biddy's had.'

He stood up. 'I won't move her. An' there's no telephone
between here and town. Will ye ride back an' git the doctor.
I'll take a look around.'

Grandmother sat, like an Easter Island figure wearing hat
and veil, in the front seat of the Ford beside Joe Speight from
the bicycle shop. She had been visiting friends at the mill.
But as they came down the hill towards the Preacher's farm
they saw Angus ride under the arched sign and turn towards
town.

'Not more trouble with the Preacher?' Joe said.

'Go faster', Grandmother said. 'Catch him up.'

Joe advanced the hand throttle but it was half a mile before
they passed Angus and stopped. He pulled in against the car.

'You've been movin' like a cut cat', Joe said. And remembered. 'Beggin' your pardon, Mrs C.'

'Is anything the matter?' Grandmother asked.

'Plenty.' Angus was breathing hard. 'The old woman's
had a stroke . . . going for the doctor.' He took a breath. 'And
the Preacher and Maudie have disappeared.'

'What do you mean, young man?'

'They've gone. Not a sign of them.'

'Joe. Back to the farm', she ordered. 'Then the doctor.'
And to Angus: 'You stay here. Joe'll pick you up.'

Grandmother had sponged the sick woman's face and hands

and was covering her with a blanket when Sergeant Scanlon returned from his search of the fields. He stamped into the kitchen and stopped.

'Mrs C. An' how did ye git here?'

'On a broomstick', Grandmother said. And relented. 'I was coming back from the mill.'

She wiped the housekeeper's lips and moistened her tongue. Only a wet mumble came when she tried to speak.

'There's nothing else I can do.'

She stood and went to the kitchen table when she untied her veil and pulled the long pins from her motoring hat. She laid the hat carefully on the table. Like flowers on an altar.

'Now Sergeant. What on earth is going on? This poor soul has been here for a day or two at least. She needs nursing. But where are the others?'

He told her the little he knew as Grandmother perched on the pine stool.

'Have you searched the whole farm?'

Scanlon shook his head. 'Part of it. There's bin little time. Dark it'll be in an hour. There's not much we can do until tomorrow – except her.'

Grandmother smiled suddenly and pointed to the kitchen chair.

'Sit down, man, and take the weight off your feet. You're no infant.'

Scanlon sat. 'I'm obliged. Me dogs are barkin' they are.'

He was too big for the room. His shoulders were nearly as wide as the doorway. He wiped his face with a khaki handkerchief.

'Trouble', she said. 'You spend your life with it. You must have a poor opinion of your fellow man.'

'There's good an' bad. Good an' bad in all of us. Take the Preacher. I tink he's a good man, or was. But too much good-ness. Like a bad sickness it is.'

125

'That's a very penetrating observation', she said. 'You always were a wise man.'

'Wise, no. Niver enough schoolin'.'

'Nonsense, man. Education doesn't give you wisdom.'

'But it helps', Scanlon said. 'It helps.'

Their eyes probed.

'What do you fear?'

'He's gone off wid her – an' I don't tink he has – or – '

'He has killed her.'

Scanlon shrugged. 'Bad blood there was 'atween 'em. Badder blood since young Angus wanted to wed her. I had a word wid the Preacher after the other trouble. On the edge the man seemed to be. All tangled inside like a fishin' line.'

She asked: 'Do you think she has been — ?' She left the question there.

But Scanlon knew and looked uncomfortable. One of his huge black boots scraped the boards.

'I don't like discussing such things wid a lady.'

'Don't be a fool, Sergeant. Do you?'

'Could be.'

Grandmother got down on her knees again to wipe the old woman's face. The Sergeant went out and looked towards the road and came back. They waited. The sun went down. A stormbird went over piping its empty call.

'Like a lost soul', Grandmother said.

Scanlon nodded.

They heard the car coming.

The rumours raced like fire through cane. The Preacher had murdered Maudie. Had raped and murdered Maudie. Had attacked the old housekeeper and run off with Maudie. Had killed Maudie and shot himself. And the rumours were sprinkled with 'I told you so', and 'Always did say that bible banging old bastard . . . .'

Early next morning, when Scanlon and his constable, armed with a police carbine, reached the farm with Angus, some of the neighbours were waiting, armed, to help in the search.

'Take the cane first', Scanlon said. 'Then we'll make for the river and turn east to the scrub. If ye find anything put a shot up.'

The men spread, moving slowly in a frayed line along the cane rows and on to the next fields and through and along them and on again to the timber and the mangroves beyond beside the water that shone like a steel plate in the early morning. Two men went upriver. The others crossed into the next farm and moved along the low bank towards the scrub like a black stain between the cane and the river. And as they approached the sleeping flying foxes stirred and scuffled in their stinking camp where the grey droppings packed with yellow fig seeds splashed the rain forest and were feet deep on every open patch of ground.

'Gawd, how they stink', one of the men complained.

Another remembered. 'In the early days they thought they were vampires.'

Then in fright, as the men came closer, and chattering and sniggering like a million dogs, they began to unhook and drop and sweep through the trees with slashing wings and lift above them where, blind in the sunlight, they circled aimlessly, black and crowded above the scrub and over the river like massed bats in some illustrated fairy tale.

Along the scrub the searchers came together in the heavy shade and rested.

'Not a ting', the Sergeant said. 'It'd take a hundred men a week to get through this stuff.'

A farmer wiped the sweat from inside his hat. 'Could be in the river. A boat might be easier to search the groves.'

'If that old devil hasn't skipped the border by this.'

'Wait a jiffy.' Another was on his feet. 'Years back – when I was a kid – a track cut through to an old boatshed.'

'If the last flood didn't get it.'

'Worth a look', Scanlon said. 'Spread out now an' see if ye can pick it up.'

The men broke saplings and beat the scrub, advancing and then working towards each other. For an hour they searched the edge.

'Here . . . pretty overgrown.'

They moved towards the shout and, sweeping the vines aside and beating the undergrowth, they pushed along the shadowy track until they could see glimpses of the river. They pushed on and emerged at last into what had once been a small clearing now covered in new growth. And among this growth the crumbling roofless boatshed above the water.

Scanlon brushed the tangle aside and found a door. He pushed and the door fell in. He stepped on top of it and into the shed followed by Angus and the constable.

'I'll murder him', Angus shouted. And rushed to her.

Maudie lay in a corner on the rotting planks. Her arms and feet were tied with old buggy reins. Her clothes were torn and filthy, as if she had been dragged across a damp field. Her face was covered in bruises and her lips split and the blood was dry at the corners. She stank.

'I'll kill him.'

Only then did the constable remember. He stepped outside, put up the carbine and pulled the trigger. The bark was deafening in the scrub and the echoes bounced up and down the river. The scrub exploded with more flying foxes.

Maudie could not speak. Not until they made a bush stretcher with their shirts and carried her back to the farmhouse and gave her a drink. Just enough at first to wet her mouth and throat. This was her third day without water. Her third day tied up, and tied also to a corner post.

Angus tried to question her, but her lips and tongue were so sore that she could only croak. She still seemed dazed, even wandering a little.

'Leave her be', Scanlon advised. 'It's a bad shock she's had.'

A farmer rode into town and, on the Sergeant's instructions, returned in the Ford with Joe Speight and Grandmother. He knew she would want to help. The doctor followed. Maudie would be all right after a day or two in hospital, he decided. The men lifted her into the back seat and, with Grandmother perched beside her, she was driven into town.

Maudie was propped in bed when Scanlon pulled up a chair at the hospital the next afternoon.

'Black an' blue an' green', he said. As if remembering evidence. 'Is it better you're feelin'?'

She nodded and tried to smile. 'I must look something awful.'

Her voice was thick as though she had a mouthful of pea soup.

'Take it easy, now. Do ye feel well enough to tell me jist what happened?'

Maudie nodded again. 'I'll try.'

She had found the housekeeper on the floor, with the Preacher's dog whining beside her. She could see that she was very ill and was deciding whether to stay with her or go for help when the Preacher, carrying his shotgun, walked in and began to scream at her. He accused her of killing the old woman. Then his mind seemed to drift. He kicked the dog which squealed out the door. He followed and took a flying shot at it as it sprinted across the yard.

'Easy now', Scanlon soothed. 'It's nicely you're doing. An' what happened nixt?'

The Preacher returned to the kitchen, grabbed her by the arm and jerked her outside and turned the key. He dragged her across the yard to the barn where he picked an old set of buggy reins from a nail. She struggled and broke free but he hit her on the face and she fell.

Scanlon looked out of the window. 'He didn't interfere wid ye in any way?'

Maudie looked surprised, 'No'.

'Then or later?'

'No. But on the way to the scrub I tried to get away again. He punched me. Many times. I felt sick.'

The Preacher led and dragged her to the scrub and through to the boatshed where he tied her up. Then he began to shout at her, rambling, on and on, until all she heard was sound beating down at her. The words like hail. She did not know what he was talking about and was too sick and tired to care. She remembered that her hands and feet did not hurt any more. Were no longer a part of her. She fainted or went to sleep. She did not know. When she woke the shed was moonlit and she was alone. She could hear the tide and the mud sucking and a mopoke calling and the scatter of possums.

She slept until daylight and he was bending over her.

'He said my name – over and over. He said, "He will never get you." Clear and only once. I was real scared then. After a bit he seemed to forget me. Then he began screaming about the sea . . . and the dogs coming in on the waves. All mixed up like. I didn't understand him. He went away after that.'

'An did ye see him again?'

'I heard him outside for a bit. He didn't come back. It got dark again. I wanted a drink bad. I could feel my tongue getting big. I thought I was going to die.'

Maudie put her hands to her face. She began to cry.

Scanlon patted her arm.

'Angus is outside – waitin' t'see ye. You'd like that.'

And went out.

CHAPTER ELEVEN

THE SERGEANT rode the district. North to where the cane land ended in timbered country. West to the foothills. For hours along the great south beach, a shimmering line ruled against the tea-tree swamps for fifty miles without a curve.

Many felt that the Preacher had gone into the river and that the king tides had taken his body to sea. But Scanlon never believed that he would suicide. A conviction based on his knowledge of the man and their common belief in God. He listened patiently to the theories but still could not agree that any man whose faith was as strong as the Preacher's, so that he knew God spoke to him through his prayers, would take his own life. Scanlon also did not believe, as most others did, that the Preacher was mad. Certainly not the madness he had seen during his long service life. Intolerant. Fanatical. Even violent. But he had always been that way. Every Saturday evening for years he had been all these things. But insane – like the people he had handled as a policeman – never. Except perhaps where Maudie was concerned. Except for Maudie. Scanlon, as he thought of the Preacher, always came back to Maudie, and to Angus.

When Scanlon returned to the station house he was exhausted, and so was his mare. She would not eat. She lay in her stall and slept. His great frame ached from days in the saddle and his brain sagged from lack of sleep. It was Easter Sunday and the first Easter Sunday Mass he had missed in his life. But his weariness was stronger.

As he was getting into bed, just after midday, Jamie was cutting through the park, across from the churches, in the black and white sunlight, on his way to borrow a book from a school friend. He noticed a man on a seat, but partly obscured, among a grove of bottlebrush and had almost reached the other side when he thought: the preacher? And nearly fell off his bicycle. Then he realised that he had only glimpsed the man through the leaves. He could easily have been mistaken. He decided to take another look. He propped his bike and, keeping trees between himself and the bottle-brush, moved back across the park. His mouth dry with rising excitement. And as he moved he heard the organ climbing at the Church of England and, more strongly, the Doxology at the Presbyterian: 'Praise God, from whom all blessings flow.' He spoke the familiar words in his head as he circled cautiously to reach a clump of bushes thick enough to hide him. 'Praise Him above, ye heavenly host / Praise Father, Son and Holy Ghost.' He parted the leaves and felt his heart frogjump and sweat warm in his hair. The Preacher was standing, holding his gun as duck shooters do. He had moved and was now framed in a space between the bottlebrush, facing the church. Then everything happened so quickly that Jamie had no time to scream a warning.

A man came first. Down the steps, putting on his hat, with others following. Jamie saw Angus and Maudie next. They stopped for a moment at the top of the steps and spoke, then moved down together, and in that instant the Preacher snapped his gun to his shoulder and fired both barrels. Jamie gave evidence later that it seemed a hurried shot, wild. The double charge just missed Angus's head and blew a hole above the door.

Long afterwards, when Jamie thought of that crashing moment, he still heard the town go still. He had never realised before how threatening silence could be. Emptiness spangled with ghosts and soundless mouths. Time clubbed into immobility, just for a moment. Before the screaming and the shouting.

Now people were pushing through the door, falling out of the church, running away from the church, along the street, anywhere except towards the Preacher and the gun he was reloading. They leapt into their traps and buggies. Horses whinnied and reared, then jerked their vehicles forward as whips lashed their flanks and they took off at a hand gallop.

Jamie saw Angus grab Maudie's arm and run with her to the back of the church. But he could think only of his grandmother. He sprinted through the trees and into the church just before the doors slammed. Women were screaming and crying and men were trying to comfort them or were peering through the windows. He found Grandmother, alone, holding her parasol like a woomera.

'I've come to get you', he said.

She put a bony hand on his shoulder. 'That was thoughtful.'

He could tell by the way she looked at him, all hard and soft and stiff, that she was pleased.

'He's coming across the road', a man called from a window.

And another, with a wider view: 'Going round the back. It's Angus and Maudie he's after.'

A woman began to sob again, a retching sound among the benches. And outside a dog howled, as chilling as a dingo call, in the empty street. The Minister climbed to his pulpit below the Burning Bush and called, quaveringly, 'Brethren, let us pray.'

'Tosh', Grandmother said. With a sniff that whistled.

She went to the door and Jamie followed.

'Open it', she ordered.

'Madam', one of the wardens pleaded. 'He's dangerous.'

'Dangerous?'

'But . . . .'

133

'If you but me, sir, I'll give you a piece of this.'

She lifted her parasol. He opened the door.

Jamie's guts were watery as they crossed the street. Like that moment when, much younger, the branch had broken and he crashed to the stable roof from the weeping fig. Now the street was a deserted beach at low tide with the sea far out and still. Lonely and scary. They skirted the park and did not look back. He took her arm and was no longer frightened when he felt the trembling.

'I'm taking you home', Jamie said.

She stopped. 'I'm perfectly capable of getting myself home. Get to the police station. Hurry.'

She gave him a push. He ran.

The shot had not wakened the Sergeant. He was curled like a troll when Jamie shook him. And tried again, more violently. The Sergeant yawned and slowly opened his eyes and stared vacantly. He yawned again, focused and said, 'Hello, young feller.'

'The Preacher.'

'What's amiss?'

'He tried to shoot Angus and Maudie – at the church.'

'So.' A long conclusive sound. 'I t'ought he was alive.'

He swung his feet to the floor and reached for his trousers.

'Git ye breath now. What happened?'

As Jamie explained the Sergeant put on his uniform and buckled on his heavy Colt. He buttoned the blue tunic to the neck, and put on his cap.

'Now you go home an' look after your grandmother.'

But Jamie followed him to the church and watched from the side of the park. He could still hear people inside the church and saw a face at a window. A group of men, two corners down, moved up the street when they saw the Sergeant.

They pointed. 'He went behind. Do you want help?'

'As much as I kin get', Scanlon said. 'I'll take a look. You spread a bit an' search the backyards. But don't take any chances.'

People were leaving the church when he returned.

'They got away', he said. 'Through Cully's garden. He heard the shot an' saw them from a window.'

'Thank God', someone said.

The others filtered back. They shook their heads.

'He could be anywhere by now.'

'That's right', Scanlon said.

Jamie, watching from the park, thought he saw a movement in a garden far down the street. Beyond the grounds of the Church of England where worshippers, unsure what had happened, peered between the trees like frightened chickens. He decided he had made a mistake and glanced back to see what the Sergeant was doing. But only for a moment. Some instinct told him to look again. The Preacher was climbing the fence.

'The Preacher', he yelled. 'The Preacher.'

Now the Sergeant was running, moving quickly for a big man. The Preacher did not hurry or look back. He seemed indifferent to the crowd outside the church. He kept on walking until Scanlon bawled, 'Preacher – stop.' Then he turned and stilled in the centre of the street, the black barrels resting across his crooked left arm. The Sergeant moved forward and halted. With five yards between them they faced each other.

'Preacher', he said, quietly. 'Be a good man now. Put down that gun.'

The Preacher did not move. His hair reached his shoulders. His long lined face seemed to have stretched. His leggings were thick with dry mud. To Jamie, he seemed to be standing in mud.

'Come wid me, Preacher. It's a quiet talk we'll be having.'

He came closer.

'Move again, and before God I will kill thee.'

The words were unnaturally loud in the silent street. Even back at the church they heard them. But they did not seem to come from the Preacher. Were not part of him. To Jamie those words were written on that spot forever.

Scanlon seemed about to speak but changed his mind. He stretched out one hand in a last appeal and stepped forward.

Jamie jumped as the gun swung and the Preacher fired both barrels. Scanlon's head, blasted off at the neck, fell to the road, bounced unevenly as a football does when it lands on an end, and rolled into the gutter. It lay, staring at the sky, with a puzzled, regretful expression. Jamie could never decide. For a moment after the explosion the great body remained upright, spurting, before the knees loosened as though they had been unscrewed and lowered it almost gently to the ground.

Even before Jamie was aware that the Preacher was running, trailing his gun, towards the lane that led to the water tower, the chilling laughter of a woman in hysterics lifted above the cries and shouts as people fled. A horse bolted, dragging a sulky with a chained wheel, so that the iron tyre sprayed fire down the street until the sulky overturned. Another horse reared and kicked its dog cart to pieces before its owner got to its head. Then the church bell began to ring, though nobody ever discovered who pulled the rope or why. A slow melancholy voice of doom the Preacher was always talking about with the certainty of preachers. The bell throbbed slowly in Jamie's head as he watched the blood from the blue body on the road and wondered irrelevantly why it was not blue as it spread and sought its own level with a slow and disgusting passion. As it reached the gutter and touched the head the dreadful marriage was too much for Jamie. Nausea washed over him and he was down, with his head being pushed between his knees. And when it was spread around him he felt better, though he still thought of the blood and the staring head with the red hair, the same colour as his own. Arms hoisted him to his feet. He mumbled thanks and saw that it was the Professor.

'Better, dear boy?'

'I'm all right.'

'Go home.'

'I'm all right.'

The Professor turned to the others. 'Where's the constable?'

'Out at Kal Kal. The cattle-stealing case.'

'Then we'll have to act without him. Did anyone see where the Preacher went?'

'Down James Street', Jamie said. 'Towards the water tower.'

The Professor was taking charge.

'How many of you can use a rifle – expertly?'

Four could, Jamie made a fifth.

'We'll get them at the station.'

The Professor pointed. 'You – go for the doctor. He'll know what to do. You – the undertaker. And you – stay with the body. Get something from the church – a curtain, anything. Cover him up.'

He knelt and found the Sergeant's keys. He unbuckled his belt, heaved the body a few inches and slid off the Colt holster. He handed it to the man who was staying.

'You could need it.'

Jamie had never seen the Professor like this before, except the day at the Boorool. And that was different. Now, as he led the way to the station, he was another person, the man he had once been perhaps, dressed in his stained jacket and filthy trousers frayed and stringy at the bottom.

The Professor unlocked the arms rack, with its six old Martini-Henrys at attention, and handed them out. They were pre-Boer War, with the kick of a Clydesdale. Then he opened the ammunition box, chained to the rack, and distributed the greasy shells.

Jackie Winn, the barber, arrived as they were leaving.

'There's another rifle inside', the Professor said. 'Round up as many men as you can and make for the water tower.'

James Street had locked itself in – except for an old man in a wicker chair in his front garden who had ignored the pleas of his neighbours. Jamie and his mates knew him as 'The Tiger'. A bad tempered old bugger with a face like a choko.

'Did you see the Preacher?' the Professor asked.

'And who would be wanting to know?' the old man said, holding his pipe and squirting.

'He killed the Sergeant', the Professor snapped. 'Now did you see him?'

'No need to get shirty. Seen him run past here. Never give me the time of day. Went through the gate to the tower.'

'Could be inside', someone suggested. And asked: 'Is the door locked?'

Jamie knew it wasn't but kept quiet. It didn't do sometimes to know too much.

'Locked', the old man spluttered. 'Not since them bloody larrikins broke the padlock two months ago.'

'We'll have to find out', the Professor said. 'He could have gone through and across the creek. Spread out until you can see the door. When I lift my arm above the fence, near the gate, give me covering fire.'

The men fired at the closed door as the Professor signalled and ran towards the white tower, but a gunshot came from one of the barred but glassless windows on the first floor. Although it spun him to the grass, he was up and behind cover almost before Jamie realised what had happened.

Jamie edged along to him. He was holding his arm. Blood spreading on his sleeve.

'A lick and a promise', the Professor said. 'Johnnie Boer was a much better shot.'

'What do we do now?' a voice called.

'Do, you riff-raff. We get below the windows from the other side, then work around to the door and rush him.'

He looked at Jamie. 'You stay out of this. Your grandmother would skin me if she knew I'd allowed you this far.'

Jamie protested but he would not listen.

'That's an order. You stay behind the fence with one of the others. Watch the windows and fire at anything that moves.'

Reluctantly, Jamie went back to his position, behind a rock outside the fence, while the men circled, crept round to the door and crashed it open. But the Preacher had been too quick. He was already climbing the iron ladders to the railed platform that circled the tower just below its domed top. Like a wedding ring sixty feet above the ground.

'We'll have to starve him out', the Professor said, while his arm was bandaged with a shirt-tail. 'He'll kill us one by one up the ladders.'

Now the people were out in James Street, jostling to get a better view, and more men were arriving with rifles and shotguns. The street was out of shotgun range, but as the attackers moved away from the base of the tower the crowd yelled a warning. The Preacher emerged on the platform far above and, leaning over the rail, fired, first one barrel, then the other. The scattering shot sang into the ground. Rifles barked but it was a high and difficult shot and when a few bullets came near him the Preacher lay on the steel platform and could not be seen from the ground.

'This could go on for days', the Professor said.

And then one of the men, a returned soldier, asked, 'What about Tommy?'

'If he's sober', the barber said. He glanced at the Professor. 'Sorry.'

'Think nothing of it, my boy. When this is over I shall be drunk for a week.'

Tommy Roberts was for once only happy tipsy. Enough to sharpen his wits and his eyesight. He had been a sniper in France but had been blown up by a shell. Even now he had a hoppy limp. He was a kangaroo shooter and the best in the district. He studied the tower from James Street and shrugged.

'Better starve him. He can get water up there by blowing a pipe.'

And then Jamie remembered. Years before he had climbed up without being caught. To smoke an early cigarette with a mate. Few people knew of the trapdoor.

'The Captain's Walk on the Old Hall', he explained. 'It's pretty high. The range isn't too far.'

Tommy grinned. 'Should've thought of it myself. You'd make a good sniper. Let's take a look.'

He went home and got his Lee Metford. The rifle with the long sniping barrel he had smuggled back in pieces in the hospital ship. Jamie showed him the way up, to the trapdoor in the little room below the Walk. Out of sight from the tower behind the iron lacework, Tommy took a good look and gave a thumbs up. He settled himself and fitted on his tube-like pinhole sight where the backsight had once been and gave a polish with his sleeve to the filed foresight.

From where he lay, with the barrel resting through an opening in the iron lace, the tower was about three hundred yards away and about twenty feet higher than the Walk, but not too high. Only part of the tower balcony could be seen. The section above James Street. The men were still firing, aimlessly now, for the Preacher was out of sight and safe.

'Patience', Tommy said. 'That's all we need. Usta have a cobber with me with a telescope. Lost a couple of 'em. Waited three days for that Hun sniper. The bastard got restless before I did. Now you go back and spread the word. No more firing.'

As Jamie went through the trapdoor Tommy grinned. 'Curiosity killed that cat.'

The firing faltered and ceased. For more than an hour they waited, watching the tower till eyes watered and necks stiffened. Watched and waited to see what the Preacher would do. The restlessness among the crowd increased.

Jamie, from behind his rock, wondered what the man above was thinking, what he was feeling. Wondered what happened inside your head when you went mad. What did you feel? Was it awful? Was it painful? What did other people look like when you were mad? He knew that the Preacher had shot at Angus and Maudie, had killed the Sergeant, had hurt the Professor. That he would kill again – kill him, kill Pearl, kill Grandmother. Yet he still felt sorry for the man above and he knew that the Professor, from something he had said, felt sorry too. A cloud went over the tower, raced to the left, fell away so that it seemed about to fall. Then the cloud passed and the tower stilled against the sky. The lonely sky like a blue tent covering the world. He thought a lot about the man up there, lost against the clouds, as they waited.

Then, challenging the rifles below, the Preacher's head appeared and disappeared. A wind seemed to brush the crowd. Then the Preacher's head emerged again and now he was standing, leaning over the rail with his gun pointing down. At that moment he jerked violently and seemed to sway and a fraction later the hard crack of the Lee Metford reached the watchers from far behind.

Jamie heard the shotgun clatter on the steel decking. Saw the Preacher sag against the rail and fold over it like a half filled sugar sack, and hang there balanced so perfectly that he felt he could stay there forever against the sky. Then, very slowly, his body spilled over the rail.

141

CHAPTER TWELVE

ALL MORNING the waggons and carts and traps rolled into town for Sergeant Scanlon's funeral. They lined the streets, wheel to wheel. There was hardly room for them along the river.

The men wore their best black suits. Taken out only on great occasions. Weddings and christenings and funerals. Their black ties drooped from stifling collars and around their sleeves and hats they wore broad mourning bands of black crêpe firmly stitched or held with hidden safetypins. Their womenfolk, too, were in mourning, but they were not allowed to go to funerals. That was not respectable. Graveside scenes, except for chief mourners, were taboo for females who by convention were insulated from the ashes of burial.

But on the morning of the funeral Grandmother suddenly decided to attend. Pearl was horrified.

'No place fer a lady.'

But Grandmother silenced her with a look.

'I daresay. But I'm going.' And added: 'I haven't been to the cemetery for years. It's time I familiarised myself.'

Pearl, about to speak, changed her mind. She looked at Jamie.

'I don't think you should', he said. Very quietly.

And felt the silent trumpet blast of their surprise.

'Why not?' Grandmother snapped.

'It's – it's not proper.'

'Fiddlesticks', she said.

But Jamie did not wilt. 'The Sergeant wouldn't like it.'

'There', Pearl said. Gathering breakfast plates.

'And why, pray?'

In her rat trap voice.

Jamie knew he must explain. He had taken a stand, the first ever on a real issue. He was not sure what to say. Yet he knew he had to convince her.

'He wouldn't like a woman at his funeral. . . . He knew how people thought. He was closer to them – closer than you are. He would know people would resent it. So he wouldn't want you there.'

He wanted to say more but didn't know how.

Pearl, still holding the plates, watched Grandmother, her arms folded implacably on the table, her eyes pinpoints of slate.

Then, very deliberately, she folded her serviette, fed it through the silver ring, pushed back her chair and went to Jamie and kissed him.

'You're right', she said. Very softly. 'Sometimes I behave like a silly old woman.'

She kissed him on the other cheek. 'I would like you to be there to represent me.'

Except for the clothes and the crêpe, Scanlon's funeral was without gloom or tears. Or any of the things Jamie associated with hearses and coffins. Even his memory of Scanlon's head in the gutter, his body on the road, seemed to have faded. Only two days before but already long ago. Like a story told last week and not properly remembered.

The bars closed at one until after the funeral. In respect for the Sergeant but also in the hope that his successor would be more tolerant about drinks after hours. As the crowd gathered the band played *Shall We Gather At the River* and other hymns on the Royal verandah, and on Preacher's Corner the five members of the Salvation Army, with a silver cornet and two tambourines, held their own public service. The Captain preached on 'Man's Eternal Sin'. And above, arguing with each other in cracked voices, the church bells made such a public nuisance of themselves that, as someone said, if Scanlon had been alive he would have put them all on a charge.

Jamie polished the car brass until he could even see the early red bristles that he now shaved every few weeks. The radiator with 'Ford' written in large slanting letters, the brass kerosene lamps and ornamental sidelamps, the long brass rods connecting the frame and the front mudguards, and even the brass hubcaps that screwed off to be filled every few months with thick golden grease bought at the hardware store in two-pound tins. And when the body gleamed with beeswax, he opened a four-gallon tin of benzine and poured it into the tank, using a funnel with copper gauze to catch the inevitable tablespoon of water that came in every tin of crude spirit. Then Joe drove the car round to Boola Street, punching impatiently at the klaxon to clear a path to the creek side of the undertakers where the other vehicles were gathering.

At two o'clock, when all was ready, Hans Schultz who, as the town said, had given up farming for a 'bloody certainty', rolled out the heavy hearse, drawn by six black horses, harnessed in pairs, from the backyard of his parlours where he announced on his front windows that the Schultz service was 'without parallel for discretion within the Empire'.

The horses were draped in black net carrying tassels on either side that nearly touched the ground, and on their collars they wore high black feather plumes that nodded as they walked. The sun flickered on the polished hearse, on the carved Greek urns that adorned its corners, on the thick glass sides of the ornamental box that were so deeply engraved that the figures stood out in smoky white relief – fat angels cavorting among a botanical garden of heavenly plants.

Sun-dried Hans, veins purpling his nose, his fair hair dyed because black was more fitting to his trade, wore a long tail coat with satin lapels, a black and white striped cravat, heavy boots and a glowing top hat. With a flourish, as though about to announce dinner at a grand reception, he opened the back doors of the hearse as the Sergeant was carried out, in the largest and heaviest coffin in the memory of the town, by six young farmers, at three shillings each for the day, with beer. And even they faltered under Scanlon's eighteen stone and the mahogany box. The town stood with hats off as the loading was completed.

Scanlon was a childless widower, but his two sisters and their husbands, who had driven from an outlying district determined not to miss the funeral, occupied the mourning coach, also pulled by a draped horse team. The blinds were half closed but wide enough for them to see and be seen, which was considered proper for chief mourners. They were important for the first and last time in their lives.

Now the band, with instruments reversed, marched down from the Royal and formed up behind the mourning coach as Hans, after a last inspection, mounted the high driving seat, reached for the black reins and carriage whip and clicked to the horses. As the traces tightened and the heavy hearse on its curved springs began to move the band, with drums and kettledrums wrapped in crêpe, blew the first wavering notes of the Dead March.

Behind the band came the Mayor in his new grey Sunbeam – far too expensive for a Mayor, the town said, suspiciously – a black Delage from the mill with polished leather straps over its bonnet and the gears outside, then a one-cylinder de Dion Bouton, a Métallurgique with a knife-edge radiator that had once reached forty miles an hour on the coast road, and Jamie and Joe in the Ford, with the hood down. Behind the Ford was Old Mick with his cab so packed with mourners that it sagged to one side, and behind the cab, for hundreds of yards, was a collection of carriages, traps, sulkies, dogcarts, spring carts and German waggons and horsemen and bicyclists.

Behind again were the Chinese, eleven of them led by Ching Fat who kept the biggest store. He was in mourning white, long gown and trousers, and below his mandarin-type cap hung his pigtail, like a black snake, which he seldom revealed but still wore in defiance of Sun Yat Sen and the new Chinese Republic. And behind Ching, royalist to his last brass button, whose shop hung tinted portraits of the Empress Dowager, Tz'u Hsi, and the infant Pu Yi, last Emperor of the Ch'ing Dynasty, came four professional mourners in rags, with sandalwood ash on their faces and hair. They paraded, but did not go all the way to the cemetery, as a courtesy to the town but with no faith that the big red barbarian in the box would join his ancestors. The professional mourners beat a heavy brass gong, slung on a pole.

The crowd, dusted by the horses and the slow turning wheels, made no attempt to disguise their feelings or to be awed by the solemnity of the day. This was a holiday added to Easter and although they were sorry that Scanlon was dead and knew that he had been a good trap, they added to the bells and the band and the crashing gong by clapping as he went by for the last time.

But the procession had moved only a few hundred yards up Boola Street when the Professor broke through the watchers, lurched against the Ford, dragged the back door open with his good hand and fell into the back seat where he recovered his breath and shook hands with Jamie in the front seat.

'My humble apologies', he said. 'Detained.'

The Professor stank. The sling supporting his injured arm was stained with grog and grime. He hadn't shaved or combed his hair. He had obviously slept in his clothes. But the crowd waved and called and the Professor, happy drunk, bowed and waved back.

'*Regardez*', he shouted, above the band and engines growling in low gear. 'There is nothing like a good funeral, or a wake, to bring out the best and the worst in people. The oldest ritual on earth. Scanlon up there, and deuced uncomfortable the poor chap must be, reminds them just for a moment of their own frail immortality.'

He tugged a half bottle of brandy from his coat pocket and swigged. Then, even before the hearse had passed the post office, his mood changed. He became serious and, always when this happened, more eloquent and more self-critical. He began to talk about himself, about the Preacher and the part he had played in his end.

'Alas, poor Preacher! I knew him, dear boy. A fellow of no jest and not an element of fancy. Driven to murder and death by his niggling demons. And why may I ask? To justify some dark stain, some lost link in his twisted and miserable heredity. Afraid of nothing but his nagging gods. Ah, goodness! What did the poet say? "Abashed the devil stood and felt how awful goodness is." Remember those words, dear boy.'

And was silent for a time.

Jamie could still see the body floating with arms and legs spread like a swimming frog, and the clouds racing sideways against the image and the tower. Still hear the bloodless cry, a sea eagle demented, as the Preacher spilt over the rail and became a shape in space. Still hear the sodden splash as the body hit and burst inside its clothes.

The procession reached the end of town and turned into Cemetery Road. The Professor began again.

'And what of the Professor?' he demanded. 'He did not fall. Icarus when the sun melted the wax that held his pinions. No, poor wandering soul. He remained earthbound, beset by his own devils who pecked at his brain, who hissed silent words

147

at him, sober and defenceless for once without his crutch, to justify his own frailties, to act the Grock before the town, to seek for once not their jibes, their sneers, their pity but their disgusting approbation. Ah, frail soul. Anxious. Cringing. Pleading. And what for? You may well ask, dear boy. Applause. Applause. Ah, respectability and the craven soul of man.'

Jamie watched him, knowing he was far away. Watched for the next half mile as he talked and talked, pouring words like seed from a bag. Words meant only for himself and for others unknown. Far away, while the black plumes ahead nodded and swayed with a sweet orchestral elegance in front of the hearse and all around was the growl of engines and the grinding of iron wheels on gravel and the clop chip of horses all conversing together as the headless Scanlon went to his grave.

'Consider Scanlon in his box', the Professor burst out again.

He could have been delivering an oration.

'Consider him', he shouted, tossing the brandy bottle into the bushes as the procession approached the cemetery. 'A simple kindly trap from Cork, an honest plodder who lost his head doing his duty. Duty, mark you well. Have you ever considered how that insignificant word hides behind the skirts of history? The sins, the crimes, the idiocies that have been committed behind its bloody little banner. The lives snuffed in its name. The pain . . . . '

The hearse turned through the gates and climbed the track to the hut where the gravedigger kept his tools and the priest waited. And, almost miraculously, the cemetery was full of life. The Professor, followed by Jamie, struggled through the weeds and over fallen tombstones and unmarked mounds to the graveside as the six farmers manhandled Scanlon and set the coffin on the boards above the grave and the burial service began as the stragglers arrived.

But as it progressed, from 'bog Irish to dog Latin', as the Professor said later, Jamie could feel that he was not giving his full attention to the last words and acts of this drama. He shifted from foot to foot, scratched his bottom, sighed, so that his neighbours were forced to back away from the brandy fumes mixed with sweat from his clothes.

At last the ropes went under the coffin and the boards were removed. The box dropped slowly out of sight. The final prayer had been mumbled, the last holy water cast, the earth crumbled to fall with that never to be forgotten sound of empty eternity. The Professor could remain silent no longer. He leapt to the mound beside the grave.

'The cold church has had its say', he yelled, so that everybody jumped like wallabies. 'Now let warm-blooded men say the farewells that Paddy Scanlon would have appreciated. He ran me in more than once but I never held it against him. A spoilsport authoritarian at times, but a good chap with a big heart. . . .'

He got no further. His boots slid on the clay that came from the very bottom of the pit. With a yell he fell head first into the grave.

Jackie Winn, the barber, was the first to laugh.

'Paddy'll charge him being drunk and disorderly.'

It was enough. The laughter swelled. Nothing could stop it. Not even the scandalized look on the face of the priest.

And Hans Schultz, not to be outdone and forgetting his dignity, slapped his thigh with his silk hat.

'Never knew they was such close friends.'

Now the scrabbling groans from below, which could not be heard before, increased in volume. The Professor, standing on the coffin, appeared above ground. Just his head, with clay in his hair and a dazed expression. The laughter began again.

'All you can do for a gentleman in distress', the Professor

growled, rubbing his head, 'is to behave like a pack of baboons in fancy dress.'

He was helped from the grave and led away from the treacherous mound. He touched a graze on his forehead with the palm of his good hand and studied the blood.

'First time you've ever been slugged by a coffin', the barber called.

'Silence, clown', the Professor yelled, nursing his injured arm. 'Unlike some people I know I have had both feet in the grave and have survived. I'm sure you will agree' – he looked around at the mourners, stopped at the priest, and went hurriedly on – 'most of you, that Scanlon, though a trifle meticulous about closing time, would not desire us to remain here any longer without wetting our whistles. The Royal is open. Our transport awaits. There is now positively nothing to detain us.'

The Professor's words acted like a starting gun. The rush began, up the slope, flattening the weeds, scattering immortelles, overturning floral tributes in urns and pots and old jam jars. The bicycle riders got away first, freewheeling down the slope and into the road. The horsemen were next, spurring and whooping. Old Mick, urged on by his passengers, at two bob a time for the ride, so astonished Emperor with his lashing that the old horse broke into a trot and the cab almost fell apart as it swayed towards the gates. Three traps and a buggy were next, but a spring cart, its owner standing and flailing with the ends of his reins, passed them and, with one wheel off the ground, reached the road first. Then came the Sunbeam, its high hunting horn a battle call, but the Delage had to be pumped before it would start and the Métallurgique refused at first to spark. Joe Speight was determined not to be beaten but he had to crank the Ford eight times before the engine fired, and at the first splutter, just as the Professor and Jamie got into the car, he was around like a rabbit and behind the wheel. He pushed the pedal, advanced the throttle and the Ford took off with a sickening lurch. Down the slope it hurtled, the Professor belabouring the front seat with his fist and shouting encouragement. The crush at the gates and in the road was so great that everyone had to slow down and even stop, but in the race for the pubs, when no driver worth his salt would allow another to pass, the vehicles were bonnet to backboard and wheel to wheel. For half a mile Cemetery Road was packed with galloping horses and swaying bodies and brandishing whips and honking car horns and shouting men. At one stage of the race, as the Professor was standing on the back seat shaking his fists and yelling abuse at the driver of the Delage who was trying to pass, a grinning horseman swept along the other side of the Ford and, bending, gave him a push that nearly sent him overboard, while just ahead the driver of a dogcart was flaying another horseman with his long whip. The Sunbeam was far ahead, but the dog cart, the Ford, the Delage, a spring cart and a rubber-tyred sulky entered the western end of broad Boola Street together with everyone yelling and screaming, in a finish, as the Professor said later, that Caligula would have enjoyed. Ahead were lurching vehicles and foam splashed horses and scattering pedestrians, and as the great race ended men abandoned their vehicles and mounts and dashed for the Royal and the Commercial to push other drinkers aside, climb over the bars and help themselves as they shouted and sang.

Scanlon's funeral was voted a bobbydazzler, the race the best since Carbine won the Cup. But the day was not yet over. Just on dark, above the roar from the hotels and the noise of people in Boola Street who had decided to make a night of it, the firebell began its chill hammering.

Jim Tucker heard it in the Commercial. And froze. Of course he had turned out the hurricane lamp. . . . He remembered going into the back storeroom . . . just before he left the shop for the funeral. But had he . . . ?

'My God', he said. Aloud.

And slammed the pot on the bar and ran.

At the same time Jamie raced from the big house just in time to see Prince, the chestnut fire horse, trot from his yard and back himself under the slung harness between the elevated shafts of the red and gold fire waggon and wait, stamping and throwing up his head. At the same time, the fireman, in his brass helmet, ran from his house, buckling on his axe belt and, reaching the firehouse, pulled the cord that dropped the harness on to Prince's back. Quickly, he buckled and tightened and leapt to the driving seat. Prince came out with a rush and turned. The iron wheels spewed sparks. The fireman, the reins in his left hand, beat the tongue of his fixed warning bell with his right as Prince broke into a canter down Boola Street where the flames were already reaching towards the top windows of Tucker's Grocery and Wine and Spirit Store.

Two of the town's volunteer firemen beat the waggon to the fire. One came by bicycle. The other ran. And one arrived ten minutes later when the fire had spread to the upper floors. But two who had been to Scanlon's funeral did not appear. By the time the engine pump on the back of the waggon had been started and two hoses had been connected to the town supply and the first bursts had been poured into the building the whole store was alight. And above the roar could be heard explosions like gun shots at a wild duck drive, as barrels and crates of bottles burst with the heat and water.

Soon out of the building and across the pavement came a stream of liquid fire that flowed into the gutter and along, a dancing flickering blue-green will-o'-the-wisp that overflowed and spread a glowing carpet on the road.

At first the watchers did not realise what was happening. Then someone shouted.

'The grog. It's the grog.'

The crowd watched through the smoke. Desperate, some of them, at the terrible waste.

Until a man went on his knees, scooped a double handful, blew the dancing fire off its surface, sucked, spat and clapped his hands to his mouth.

'Gawd', he spluttered. 'Red bloody hot. But bloody beaut.'

Only then did all the watchers fully understand that the liquid fire was burning spirit. Free spirit. The rush began.

They sprinted to the hotels. Broke down the doors and windows of shops. Converged on the flowing grog with beer mugs, bottles, vases, battered tins – any utensil they could find. And as the word spread they came from the houses bordering Boola Street, and from streets further away, carrying buckets and saucepans and rusty benzine tins and even washing tubs to ladle the endless gift of burning whisky, brandy and rum mixed with gin and wine and water and carry it away and return for more, while others scooped with mugs and tumblers, blew the fire and the heat from the liquor and drank.

The hot mixture exploded in bellies already suffering from the celebration after Scanlon's funeral. Soon the street was littered with bodies. One man lay beside the still flickering stream and tried to lap. Another fell into the horsetrough and slept. Others folded in doorways or staggered up or down the street until they fell or wandered off singing, shouting, cursing.

The walls of the burning building collapsed and drenched the street in sparks and smoke. The firemen, who had been liberally supplied with liquid fire, continued to spray the buildings on either side of the glowing wreckage until the hoses fell from their hands and, dropping beside the red and gold waggon, they too slept.

Prince stood, as he had been trained, without moving. Looking down at the writhing hoses still pumping. A body in the centre of the street got up and staggered away and collapsed again. A heap of burning rubble scattered fire-works. Part of a wall fell in. The pump on the fire waggon coughed, missed a beat and stopped. The brass hose nozzles stopped wriggling and lay still. Gently pouring now at Prince's feet.

CHAPTER THIRTEEN

LONG AFTERWARDS, when talk echoed to Scanlon's funeral and the fire, when the essence of that day had, like good wine, matured, townsfolk still recalled, and many with hilarity, incidents from the funeral or that one evening when practically everyone in town was drunk.

But in the immediate days and weeks the town's conscience itched and a collective unease that came close to shame, especially when they remembered the stampede for the flaming grog, led many to evade the revealing details of that one besotted evening.

Jamie climbed the mango tree soon after the fire and breathed in the spicy glue from its bleeding trunk. Looked across the town, beyond where the wine and spirit store was now a broken tooth, and knew again that another strand had been spun in the web of his existence. The mood that poured back to him through his eyes was new. A hot yearning emptiness in his guts. But impossible to explain.

He gazed upriver to the island where the sea eagles lived and wondered, just for a moment, how they could see a water rat a hundred feet below. And knew, with the violence of a door slamming, that the change he was conscious of had nothing to do with the town. It was not outside, hanging upside down like a flying fox, but within. Deep within. So much had happened. Horror, pain, even death. And so quickly, and with such terrible logic, that being alive was a new and throbbing awareness. Landing on the beach of a strange country. Not an awareness of physical things but of moods and desires, of excitement and wonder and hunger and sounds in the dark like lost birds.

When he was younger he remembered the stench of new leather, tanbark and old boots, the cold impersonal smell of tools, the dust on fraying hides. The bootmaker – hair like a worn brush, steel pebble spectacles close to his eyes, hands stained and creased with leather and work. A sour uncommunicative man who grunted answers as he cut and sliced and hammered, brass tacks feeding from mouth to sole and hammer head in a calculated stream in his shop across the river.

Now Jamie knew better, knew the reason for his apparent churlishness. The cobbler's invalid wife. The cobbler going slowly blind. But with so much patient courage that even now he often mended with eyes closed, teaching his unseen fingers, testing his hidden aim, perfecting his craftsmanship against the time when he would be able to continue, if God willed, making boots and restoring soles when the inevitable darkness came.

He remembered, too, asking Pearl why she did not have a husband. Asking in innocence and ignorance and being shoved in anger from the kitchen. Not knowing why then, ignoring the expression in her eyes, the flick of fear, the hopelessness. Gone in a flash and not understood until now. Feeling her anguish turning to resignation for what might have been. A little death. Slow gathering each day and week into endless lonely months and bitter years.

Jamie knew then that the remembering and the knowing were two worlds. The past and the now. As separate as the sea and the land, for the point of contact did not matter. The waterline was never the same. Even the beach dried with the movement of the tides and became another place. He could feel the sides of his chrysalis cracking.

And then, in the next few weeks, he saw that the parrots

were moving south again and, watching them streak across the town, calling, calling, he wanted to follow them, to probe and explore, to know more about life and girls and the things they did to you and the things that were only hinted at in books. Some afternoons he chopped wood for Pearl until the axe was almost too heavy to lift or he wheeled out his bike and drove for miles until the wild longing for the unknown eased. But it always returned, stronger. More unendurable than before.

He watched the birds and thought of their exquisite freedom to come and go, to eat and nest and die. Their cycle of arrival and departure and arrival. A clock turning, always on time. Inevitable and mysterious. Force and counter-force. Certain. Wonderful.

He watched the parrots, knowing that each year at summer's end they came north to escape the first chill winds of the deep south, across the plains and mountains he knew only on a map. Across his grandmother's far beckoning Murrumbidgee and the snow below Kosciusko. They came a thousand miles and more and went on another thousand to the hot northern ranges against the Coral Sea to mate and nest. And before the next summer they came south again, thick wedges of screaming colour, fast moving smudges on the clear blue or in demented arches of green and turquoise and crimson across the gleaming roofs of the town. Going north or going south, their high screaming tore the daylight, rinsed the clouds, and at dusk they made arabesques that filled the trees and strong boughs swayed and sagged under the weight of tens of thousands. Sleeping. Until the next daylight drove them on.

This year, as the first flights returned from the north, more numerous than ever he felt, Jamie was ready. He made good pocket-money catching and selling the Greenies and Blueies to people who liked to cage them and others who made steaming parrot pie. He got out his black horsetail snares, each with its running noose, that he had laboriously plaited, and tied them securely to his catching pole. They covered the pole from tip to base and gave it an unbrushed look like the Professor's hair. Then he lashed the pole to the fowlhouse, so that the tip was twenty feet above the Morning Glory on the tin roof. And with this completed he caught his best caller, a large Blue Mountain, in the parrot house, put him in his special box with a wire mesh top so that he could be seen and put the box at the base of the pole beside a larger receiving box fitted with a spring lid. A heap of sugar bags beside this box and he was ready. He retreated to the feed room at the stables to wait.

His caller began, reluctantly, since he had been long caged, but with growing interest and urgency, to answer the screeches of the passing flights and soon was trying to match call for call. The first dozen flights were high, some little more than blurs in the blue. The wild birds didn't hear the caller or they ignored his appeals and were out of sight in seconds. Then a lower flying group heard and responded. In a screeching sweep they came round and down to land in a fluttering splash of polished colour on the Morning Glory, on the caller's box, on the hairy pole.

Jamie waited. Just long enough for hooked feet and heads and even beaks to become encircled. Then he clapped his hands. Once. The parrots were gone, hundreds of them, in a detonation of feathers, before he reached the ladder. But the trailing nooses held ten as the wild things struggled, in the only way they knew, to fly. One snapped the snare before he reached the fowlhouse roof and escaped, but the other snares held. He grabbed a bag and with it the lowest parrot dangling from the pole and released the noose from its leg and dropped it into the receiving box. And all the time he was in confusion of splashing wings and screeches and clashing beaks as they struck at his face, his ears, his hands, his clothes. One big Greenie bit through the bag, deep into his finger, and another strangled itself before he could lower the pole. But eight in the parrot house from the first call of the day was a profitable beginning. He tied on more snares, opened nooses that had closed during the struggle, lashed the pole again and went back to the feed-room.

But that evening, with the parrot house crowded, he saw them for the first time. As prisoners, their great flights over. As he watched the beautiful things through the wire, he thought of the south where he too wanted to go, where they would never go now, and felt, with alarming certainty, that this would be his last season to cage his caller and anchor his snares. He wondered why the thought had come to him. The only answer was the harsh screeching.

Jamie turned and drifted back to the marshlands of sleep. It was snowing and he wondered what snow felt like between his fingers, on his arms, on his tongue. He reached for the flakes and tried to touch them. Reached too far and was awake and the garden was drenched in butterflies. Torn tissue paper, white flickering falling drifting. Moving across the flowers, under the mango tree, over the fence and up across the buildings and away.

His grandmother had told him, when he was very small, that white butterflies were the souls of children and he still believed it, not because he thought it was true but because the explanation appealed. He liked the idea that it could be true. Just as her other story, that thunder was the carts bumping along the rough roads of heaven, enchanted him so much that beside it all other explanations were as dull and unappetising as lemon sago pudding.

He got out of bed and went into a sunlit morning of moving white where the butterfles flowed over and around him.

Touching brushing dusting. If they landed it was only for a moment as they tested with frail golden legs and inquiring antennae. Then they went on, driven by a force, gentle but relentless, some dynamo urge beyond comprehension. Millions had already passed through and millions were coming. From so far away they seemed the last of the early morning mist. Across the river, above the river, among the fig trees and the silky oaks. All moving at the same speed, not hurrying or changing direction. A limitless pattern of fluttering white spread across the river and the town.

The migration continued for three days, faltered and began again. The few that drifted to the ground were dead, so that the flight of death was as natural as the flight of life. The birds dived on the butterflies but made no impression. Soon they became so gorged they preened their feathers among the golden silky-oak flowers and ignored the endless drifting food.

The butterflies were followed by a time of such profligacy that even old-timers recalled nothing like it before. The swallows, which had deserted their mud nests on the water tower on the day of gunfire, now returned, eager, darting, to make lovely fish patterns with wings and tails against the white stone, against the sky. The river was angry with salmon, slim arrows fired for the spawning upstream where the water became brackish above the rapids where the wild castor-oil plants grew in reddish thickets. The koalas fed up to the fringe of the town, as they had from the beginning, but more of them this year, grunting and coughing among the whimpering leaves. Colonies of them so that Jamie could count twenty and thirty together in a few trees. And in the sunlit fringes of the scrubs the big brown snakes and the white and red belly blacks and even the thin green tree snakes, clotted in copulating heaps that resembled big fresh pads of squirming simmering cowdung.

The sky whistled with ducks and teal and quail, plover piped across the river flats and out to the swamps; pheasants, balancing with elegant tails, hooted and answered from the bush. All day Jamie was conscious of the complaint of birds, the shadows of blue and white herons, the laboured flights of ibises, both white and black, the predator shags skimming the river, the chill of curlews, the far-off haunting protests of stormbirds. And at night the black arrowheads of swans, group following group, hundreds together and packed so close they seemed solid, flying south, their leaders trumpeting. Streaming across the town, so low over the big house that the air pulsated with their wing thrusts and the top leaves of the mango tree rattled and stilled, rattled and stilled.

Then Jimmy Purton, who farmed the Big Bend down river, brought in alarming news. He had been on benders before so that nobody would believe him. Not at first.

'Thought I'd been on the booze again, didn't you?' he told a group outside the blacksmith's.

He had heard the rumbling bellow of a bull in his bottom paddock along a tidal creek that dissected his farm. But he kept no cattle, except a few milkers, and they were grazed near the farmhouse. And his neighbours did not own a bull. He checked the bottom paddock. No print or dung or broken fences. Then, in the creek mud, in a space between the mangroves, he saw the splayed prints and the drag of a body. He had lived further north. He knew. The bull he had heard in the night had been a bull crocodile.

Crocodiles had never been so far south and farmers with waterfront properties were alarmed. Were the northern crocs changing their habits? Was the sea becoming warmer and encouraging them to migrate? Nobody could answer their questions but crocs in the river where they had been unknown posed a new danger. Jimmy and other farmers patrolled their creeks and watched at night but at first no trace was found. The doubtful became sceptical. Jimmy had been known to see and hear things before. So Jimmy, to prove his integrity, decided to set a bait. He tied a goat to a stake beside his creek. The sceptics waited. It wasn't touched. The sceptics laughed. Then a morning later goat, stake and rope were gone and in the mud, before the crabs could wipe them out, were the unmistakable prints and the body drag.

But from that day live bait and poison meat went untouched. No other signs were seen. Watchers wearied of sitting up with rifles ready and abandoned the hunt. The crocodile was never heard again and its tracks were never seen again. Everyone assumed it must have been a loner and that it had gone north again to the warmer waters beyond Capricorn. But Jimmy became part of the history of the district, for on old maps his creek is still marked, 'Purton's Croc Creek'.

Jamie thought of the crocodile as the half-way point in that prolific year. Questioned, then and later, whether there could be any link between its wayward migration to waters its kind had never frequented before and the mass drift south of the white butterflies. Why south, he asked himself? Why his own urge? Was he too attracted by the force that tugged at insects and animals? Even the dog packs earlier in the year had all been southwarding as though driven by some unendurable pressure.

But even the crocodile was forgotten in a new excitement. Overnight, Boola Street was splashed with black and white posters. A flying machine was coming. A real aeroplane.

CHAPTER FOURTEEN

THE HEAPED brushwood had just been fired when Joe Speight drove Grandmother and Jamie to what was ever afterwards the 'Landing Ground'. A rectangular paddock fenced with stunted gums on three sides a mile beyond the cemetery and the only open grass near town where, in the opinion of men who had been in France, an aeroplane could land.

Smoke from the signal fire, which the coming aviator had requested as a guide, lifted in a pipe until it reached treetop level. Then the currents spread it over the paddock and over the crowd gathered to welcome the first aeroplane most of them had ever seen.

The Mayor waited beside his Sunbeam. The Mayoress in the front seat nursed a bouquet of mixed flowers, ready for the distinguished visitor. A great occasion that demanded a civic reception on the historic landing spot. A speech of welcome.

The aeroplane was due, the posters had said, at ten o'clock. Captain Arthur Shields, ex-Royal Flying Corps, and his mechanic, Mr Thomas Prentice. On an 'aerial tour of the north'. No wonder the town was almost deserted.

The crowd watched the southern sky, looking for an alien speck above the trees. Watched until their necks ached. Until a watcher shouted, 'There it is'. Pointing excitedly. Until another shouted back, 'It's an eagle, you mug'. The crowd, amused, stirred like a jumper ant's nest. They faced south, most of them unsure what to expect.

But the small brown biplane caught everyone looking the wrong way. It came in from the north-west, just above the trees, so that aeroplane and engine roar arrived almost together. It banked and circled the smoke filled paddock and wagged its wings. The surprised crowd waved and cheered.

'Must've followed the river', Joe said. 'Read somewhere that's how they find their way.'

'They follow railway lines, too', Jamie said.

He had read it in the *Boy's Own Annual* a couple of years before.

Now the biplane was coming in, over the end of Kelly's farm, over the track between the last of the cane and the paddock. Down with a strange tearing rush, the wind whistling in its struts, as the black helmet in the front cockpit reached out a gloved hand to a switch on the outside of the fuselage and the engine cut and the machine was down and bouncing, its wings and ailerons flapping, towards the enveloping crowd.

In the rush the Mayor was pushed aside and the bouquet knocked from his wife's hand and trampled, and the aeroplane itself was saved from being crushed only when returned soldiers formed a ring around it and held the excited crowd back as Captain Shields climbed up and sat on the back of his cockpit and removed first his gloves, then his goggles and then his flying helmet before swinging his legs over the side to footplates on the lower wing.

He was tall and thin with black hair and a clipped French moustache. He wore a leather coat over a brown tweed jacket, a soft shirt and tie, flying breeches of fawn twill and brown polished leggings above brown boots. His mechanic, in white overalls and a beret, followed.

The Mayor at last reached the machine, red and breathless from pushing, followed by the Mayoress whose hat had been crumpled and ruined, to welcome the 'intrepid aviator' who had brought 'great honour and distinction to our town'.

But nobody listened. They were far too interested in examining and commenting on their first aeroplane with its flimsy fabric body, thick wired struts, polished propeller and even the top of the black joystick that could be seen in the front cockpit. And in the mechanic's beret, a headstyle that was as new and strange as the aeroplane, and in the aviator's moustache and tightly encased stovepipe legs.

At last the Mayor raised both arms and shouted for silence above the noise of the crowd.

'Captain Shields has requested me to inform you all that as he will be here for only one day, before continuing this first historic tour by aeroplane of the north, he will be available immediately for joy flights of short duration over our renowned and beautiful district. The fee is more than reasonable for an experience of a lifetime. Five pounds, and ten pounds for anyone courageous enough to stunt with him – to perform the famous Loop the Loop, the Side Slip, the Falling Leaf and other aerial gyrations.'

The crowd gave three cheers and waited expectantly to see who would be crazy enough to be first to leave the ground in that contraption. But when no volunteers offered the Mayor again raised his arms.

'Come, come, ladies and gentlemen – fellow citizens. This is a magnificent opportunity to experience the thrills of flight, the conquest of gravity itself, in your first flying machine. I ask. Nay. I appeal. Is the spirit of adventure dead in us?'

From the back of the crowd a black parasol was raised.

'I will take the first ten pounds worth.'

People near Grandmother sniggered and some even laughed. She could not be serious. Then some clapped. Then everyone was yelling and arguing.

'But you can't', Jamie hissed at her. Scared for her, yet envious.

'Can't I, boy', she snorted. 'You watch.'

The crowd made a pathway. She advanced and held out her hand to the aviator.

'Young man. I shall be delighted to Loop the Loop with you. And all the other newfangled things you do up there.'

'But, Madame', Captain Shields said. And got no further.

'No buts. When you issue a challenge you must honour it.'

'Naturally', he said. 'But . . . your age.'

'Young man, that is my responsibility. Steam and I were babes together. I was a girl when the *Great Eastern* crossed the Atlantic Ocean. I am quite determined to see the earth from a flying machine before I die. Are you ready, sir?'

The Captain looked desperately at the Mayor, at his mechanic.

'You challenged anyone', a man called.

'Aren't you game?'

The crowd began to chant. 'One . . . two . . . three . . . four . . .'

'Very well', the Captain said. 'I am at your service, Madame.'

He glanced at Joe and Jamie. 'Perhaps your two sons will help you up.'

'Thank you for the compliment', Grandmother said. 'You *will* fly far.'

Only then did Jamie realise, with a shock, how much this last adventure meant to her and how determined she was not to miss it. His disappointment at not being offered the flight left him. He was no longer envious. He understood and was happy for her.

The crowd roared approval as she put on the big leather coat the mechanic handed her. They roared as Jamie and Joe, with the Mayoress holding down Grandmother's long skirts, hoisted her up, with the help of a foothole in the fuse-lage, into the observer's cockpit. The Captain buckled her in, gave her a flying helmet and showed her how to put it on. She handed Jamie her bag and hat and Joe her parasol and fitted on the broad goggles.

The Captain climbed into his cockpit and pulled on his helmet. The mechanic ducked under a wing and tugged down at the propeller. The engine made a wet sucking. The Captain reached for the switch outside the cockpit and held up a gloved hand.

'Contact.'

The mechanic gripped high and swung, down and away. The engine coughed like a horse with strangles. He swung again and then again and the engine exploded with life. The fabric body shuddered like a jelly and seemed about to fall to pieces. Hats sailed away in the slipstream and, to the secret delight of all the men, flattened dresses showed too much of ladies' figures. The crowd scattered as the machine, the mechanic pushing on one wing, turned and taxied and turned.

It roared bumping along the paddock, its tail skid tearing at the grass. Then the tail lifted and it was off the ground, climbing and heading down river. But it soon returned, much higher now, to do a Side Slip and an Immelmann Turn that made the watchers hold their breaths and ah. Then the machine dived and climbed and Looped the Loop. Once. Twice. Three times. The crowd screamed in excitement and fear. But when it was level again and they heard the engine stop and the machine began to flutter down – 'like a dying butterfly', Jamie thought, with horror – they panicked.

'It's falling down', a woman screamed and fainted.

Others covered their eyes or turned away.

'Get out', Joe Speight yelled, not realising what he had said.

People were crying and wringing their hands as they watched the aeroplane fluttering down in the Falling Leaf, and a man, his hands clasped in prayer, called, 'Dear God, save the poor old lady'.

Then, far above, they heard the engine splutter and roar again. The helpless side to side wing flutter stopped and the machine steadied and banked and circled. Soon it was down, bumping like an angry beetle across the grass.

The mob surrounded the aeroplane, yelling and screaming questions, as Grandmother was helped out. She took off her helmet, reached into her bag and handed the Captain ten one-pound notes.

'Young man, I'll let you know if I ever get closer to heaven.'

'You deserve to', he said. 'You're the best passenger I ever took up. But five pounds is enough.'

As he handed back the other five he asked, 'What did you honestly think of flying, Madame?'

'Interesting', she said, pinning back her hat. 'But not half as exciting as chasing kangaroos through timber on a half-broken horse.'

To the astonished envy of the town Captain Shields took thirty pounds in the day before he barnstormed on, following the coastline north because, as he told the Mayor, not knowing the country he could always land on a beach if his engine stopped.

'Think of it', a commercial traveller said sourly as the cab swayed up Boola Street. 'Thirty quid. Enough to keep a whole family for a couple of months.'

'Two months', Old Mick called back from the driving seat. 'It's six hundred bluddy fares to the station. If I whispered that to Emperor the poor beastie'd sit down in the shafts, he would, an' give up the ghost.'

And then, almost overnight, it was Show time and the visit by the brown biplane and Grandmother's first flight were events to recall and argue on winter nights.

Jamie knew when he woke, aware under the net of the smell of elephants. The sweet stench of their straw dung, the soft clash of their chains in the thinning dark as they pulled the covered waggons and the boarded cages from River Street on to the grass around the fig tree.

He lay back, hearing again one of his first sounds to puncture the silence of his infancy, and was glad. In a glowing voiceless way. Knowing that in the morning, only an hour or so away, the sunburnt tent would be spread ready for lifting, the horses and ponies tethered along the fence above the river, the town echoing to steel stakes hammered with light sledges, the boys wagging from school and touting for odd jobs and free tickets for the first matinee.

Jamie had never fully recovered from his first circus. Already a lifetime away. So stunned with wonder that Grandmother thought he must be sickening for something. The nameless smell of sawdust and horses and caged animals and elephants and powdered ladies. The unforgettable sounds of hammering, rumbling lions, mad donkey laughter, trumpet scales, shouts of working men. The dust that lifted from the ring to the high swinging lights, so that everything inside the tent, ring and animals and benches and people, existed through a curtain of gauze.

Glitter, sequins, spangles. Unforgettable make-believe from beyond the stars. Horses' tails and manes plaited with red white and blue ribbon. The sad makeup of the grinning clowns. The scarlet hussar uniforms of the attendants. The ring master in black tail coat and top hat spanning the gauze with his silver whip. The rippling rolling kettledrums. The never-ending brassiness of the band that thumped inside his head for days and days afterwards.

The Grand Parade, a procession in colour direct from an adventure story in *Chums*. Danny and his Marching Geese. Major Gideon and his Lions which snarled and reached for him with open claws and almost made Jamie wet himself with fright. Red Indians on piebald horses. Cossack riders with bandoliers and astrakhan caps. The Pink Fairy dancing on a white gelding's back. The Chinese Fire Eaters. The Flying Amazons beyond the floating gauze of the trapeze. Augustus the Clown who rocked a high chair, then fell over backwards and travelled round the ring suspended from the tail of Alice the elephant. He knew them all.

The circus came in the dark and disappeared in the dark. That was part of its magic. It left nothing but seeds from feed bags and the seeds became sprouts of corn and sorghum and wheat that soon withered. The circus was a mystery out of nowhere, going nowhere. From the hidden world beyond the river and the black scrubs came faces sounds smells colours. A visit of wonder and excitement that left only seeds on the grass and little pictures in Jamie's mind to last forever.

The circus came and went with Show time when Grandmother gave her annual ball. Twenty couples in the arched dining-drawing rooms of the big house. A good way to return hospitality and get it over with, and every year she announced that it would be the last and always changed her mind. Jamie remembered, too, that every year she protested that the behaviour of the younger generation, and by that she meant people in their twenties, thirties and even forties, was sadly deteriorating and that their manners left much to be desired. A guest who had tossed a bread roll at supper was never asked again.

The ball was for grownups but for the first time Jamie, who was nearly seventeen, was allowed to attend, though not to take part. Grandmother even ruled that he was still too young to wear evening dress. He helped erect the supper marquee on the lawn beyond the mango tree and clear both rooms of furniture before preparing the floor, since any ball with a slow or sticky floor was a failure from the first waltz. He cleared the rooms, after rolling up the heavy carpets, and then covered the boards with a mixture of candle shavings and powdered boracic acid and worked this in. Then he filled a bag with sand and dragged it up and down and across until the floor reflected and was so glassy that he could slide almost effortlessly from end to end. He also created an alcove of potted palms and plants on the verandah for the band of piano, violin, accordion and kettledrums and put a claret cup and fruit cup table at the other end of the verandah for the big bowls that, early in the evening, and unbeknown to Grandmother – though sometimes guests wondered about this – would be so well laced from silver and leather flasks that the ladies would be giggling by ten o'clock.

Jamie, though still an onlooker, enjoyed the excitement and laughter of these evenings. The dreamy swirling waltzes, the stamping of the Lancers, the men like spotless penguins, the women in long gowns, their shoulders powdered, their high-corsetted breasts half showing, the perfume and the fire of diamonds on fingers resting on black shoulders, the subtle sweet faintly tainted smell of many women. Even when the furniture had been restored, and for many days, he could still detect it about the house, the woman smell that was both a warning and a challenge. The men, he noticed, despite their high stiff collars and white ties and shining lapels, looked little different than they did in the street, but the women – all were more beautiful, even the ugly, as though they had suddenly awakened. It showed in their smile and in their eyes. Especially their eyes. To Jamie they were like gazanias in the garden opening to the first warmth of the sun.

During the evening Jamie was watching from a doorway, enjoying the music, swaying and swinging inside to the sweep and spin of the dancing couples, feeling apart yet part of the gaiety, when Mary's mother broke from her partner and kissed him.

'You're getting so handsome I could eat you', she said.

And went off smiling back at him, her fan and little pink programme dangling from her wrist.

He felt violently old and young and shy. In a perfumed haze. Still feeling her lips, and liking their touch. And wanting it to happen again and hoping it wouldn't in front of all the guests. Still hearing her voice and what she had said. But thinking not of her but of Mary. Embarrassed, he escaped. To the kitchen to help Pearl. And as he carried the last things to the marquee he heard the band begin the supper dance.

Supper among the flowers and streamers and balloons and laughter. Midnight for the next couple of hours. Not supper really. A banquet, since a ball without turkey and sucking pig and goose, trifles and pies and jellies, fruit and chocolate and champagne, was not a ball at all. A meal guests expected, with bowls of steaming soup in the early hours before the men changed their patent leather dancing pumps for street shoes and boots and took their wives home.

Jamie did not wait for this last ritual. He went to bed and dreamt of the woman who had thrown him an apple through the window of the Royal dining room. Centuries before. And the parted lips that had framed 'catch' as the apple spun towards him. Only in the dream it was not the same woman. Another in a crimson dress that swished as she moved towards him. Another. With Mary's eyes.

CHAPTER FIFTEEN

THE TOWN closed for two days at Show time, dressed in its best and went to the Oval. A natural bowl in the bush off the southern road where the ring was circled by a cycling track of powdered red ant-bed wet rolled like a tennis court into a hard and treacherous surface.

The sideshows clung to the ring. The small grandstand, draped in flags and bunting, was opposite. Behind the grandstand the Exhibition Pavilion, a long galvanized iron shed, almost overflowed with fruit, vegetables, flowers, cakes, jams, sugar cane and needlework. And behind again another tin shed held the bar run by the three hotels. A place of savage rites, forbidden to those of Jamie's age. Of shouts and fights and wild laughter that lifted above the thumping of the band in mid-ring among kicking horses and flying wood chips and the gravel megaphones of the sideshow spruikers.

When the town was a mining camp and the first Shows were organised for sports and feats of strength, an unwritten local rule demanded that as many people as possible should take part. And although the character of the Show had changed with the years, the old rule persisted and everyone who could competed in the events.

Jamie came last in the Beginners' Sprint but enjoyed the scramble after the bell, the wind in his hair, the flick of watching faces, the whine of tyres driving for the finish. He competed in the Under Eighteen Twelve Inch Cut and came third and then watched the new event on the programme, the

Michael Scanlon Memorial Tree Felling Championship, a contest for five guineas and a silver cup that was already known, with irreverent brevity, as 'Paddy's Chop'.

Jamie, with his height and long reach, though he was still too thin for his six feet, then lasted three jolting rounds and earned five shillings against the 'Loo Kid at Kelly's Travelling Troupe. And he was still dabbing his nose, outside the tent of the Bearded Lady, when he bumped into Miss Pringle, his French teacher at the high school.

'What on earth has happened to you?' she asked.

He told her. How the 'Loo Kid had got through with a straight left and nearly knocked him out in the first seconds of the fight.

She laughed. Low and warm.

'You could have been hurt. Badly, I mean. They're professionals.'

He saw a new Miss Pringle in her long white dress and wide straw. Different from the teacher in front of the form laying down the law on French grammar. Or bending forward in her loose blouse but never far enough for the boys in the front rows. Looking down at her he realised, almost with a shock, that he had never really seen her before. She was plain, except for her wide curving mouth and her green eyes slanted up at him. He liked how her long dark brown hair, usually coiled at the back, was now plaited and worn, like small cow pads, over her ears. No longer the teacher. Another person. Yet not quite a stranger.

And then, with her eyes smiling into his, he felt tongueless, with arms too long and feet boats. Stiff and awkward as a colt. He said, desperately, 'I won five bob. Would you like – a stone ginger?' Not thinking she would accept.

She did not seem to notice how the words had tripped each other.

'I'd love to', she said.

174

They went to the soft drink tent and found a table to one side. The ice, chipped from a block in a tub, was friendly in the thick glasses. He felt more at ease. No longer awkward and inadequate.

She drank and put her handkerchief to her nose.

'It's the snizzles', Jamie said.

'The what?'

'When the fizz races up your nose.'

She laughed. Again slow and friendly. As though she enjoyed laughing.

'What other words have you invented?'

'Cruffles. The sound your feet make in dry leaves.'

'I like that. I can hear it. Dry and musical.'

And added, raising her eyes from her brown hands, 'You're a rather unusual young man.'

He had never been called anything like that before. He liked it but could find no reply. At last he said: 'I feel different.'

'How different.'

'I'm not sure. Separate perhaps.'

'Superior?'

'No, not that. I don't want to mix with everyone.'

'Solitary?'

'A little.'

She did not pursue but asked: 'What do you hope to do later. University?'

'I've thought of a lot of things.' He felt more comfortable. 'Farming. Even a doctor. But there's the war. I'll be eighteen next year.'

'Oh, no', she said. 'It'll be over by then.'

They were silent. That word seemed to have crawled between them.

At last she said: 'You mentioned farming. You don't look like a farmer to me.'

'What does a farmer look like?'

She smiled. '*Touché.*' And changed the subject. 'Your English master tells me you write well.'

'I like writing. Essays and things.'

And thought: So they talk about us.

'Writing's easier than talking.'

'To me?'

'No – not you.'

She lifted her glass. Her eyes were amused. But they did not mock or condescend. As older eyes sometimes did. From superior heights.

'I suppose you think I'm quite ancient', she said.

The words were unexpected. But for the first time he smiled. Freely.

'Not ancient but . . . but older than I am.'

'I'm twenty-three', she said.

'I thought you were much older.' And felt foolish.

She laughed. 'Do you think I'm pretty?'

Jamie struggled. The teacher again.

'No, but . . . .'

'Yes.'

'You're not pretty, but . . . .'

'Yes.'

'You're nice . . . and . . . and . . . .'

'And what?'

'Warm.'

He couldn't think of anything else, but she reached out and touched his hand.

'That's a perfect compliment.'

He didn't feel foolish any more.

She rose. 'I must go. I have enjoyed our talk. Thank you.'

She left the tent as he paid for the ginger. When he reached the sunlight she was nowhere to be seen. He was glad and disappointed, relieved and yet intrigued. He was still thinking of Miss Pringle when he reached the saddling paddock as Mary was dismounting.

'Did you win?' he called across the rail.

'Of course', she said, swinging the reins as she led the jumper towards him. 'Do you mean to say you didn't watch?'

'I was thirsty', he said.

'If you were a bit older I'd say just like a man.'

The arrow landed but did not pierce. He grinned at her. They were used to each other. A wisp of yellow hair blowing across her forehead under the bowler. Her reef water eyes smiling. Her red mouth.

'Gosh', he said, 'you look stunning.'

The words astonished him. He had not meant to say them. But he didn't want to run, to hide.

He felt her watching, not just looking. As Miss Pringle had. Measuring as women did. Calculating and pleased.

She dropped him a mock curtsy. 'Thank you, kind sir.'

They were the same age and had known each other since childhood. They had played and swum together, and sometimes fought. Once she had split open his ear with a cricket bat after he had pulled her pigtails. Yet they had never seen each other before. Until this moment. A second of startled awareness. Flick of a wing.

But Jamie's greatest shock that day was Pearl. Among the whine of the fairy floss machines spun by hand, among a clutter of coloured hats and balloons and bakelite humming birds on long sticks, he saw Pearl and beside her a man holding out a wrapping of pink floss. There was too much noise to hear but she smiled and her lips spoke as they turned away. Towards the ring and the grumble of the crowd.

Pearl with a man was as exotic as Grandmother breasting the Royal bar and demanding a pot of beer. Jamie knew most people, at least by sight, but he had never seen this man before. He suspected from his stiff clothes that he was a farmer and guessed from what Grandmother called the 'Bavarian look' that he was German. But much older than Pearl, with a lined face and thick greying moustache and a pale grey felt hat hardly dented in the crown.

Jamie followed but lost them in the crowd. Then, as though impaled, he stopped as the band began to play in the centre of the ring. Not the usual march music or Gilbert and Sullivan or bits from *Chu Chin Chow*, but music that was foreign, that seemed to have no place at a fair. It ebbed and soared and spoke to him, so that he felt he was the only person in all that crowd who heard and understood. It lifted through the dust haze from the ring, elegant and haunting and somehow everlasting. It no longer seemed to come from the band but from the sky. Drifting down to him like the first mist of rain. Drifting and rising and returning. It spoke a strange language. Of hope and beauty, perhaps. Timeless. The music made him sad and at the same time glad and grateful and taller and new in a strange tumultuous way.

The last gliding note of a silver trumpet and he was thinking of Mary and her yellow hair and for days he saw her face across the saddling paddock rail and from above came the music playing endlessly until Mary and the music were part of each other, part of a whole, part of him, part of them both.

Not long after the Show Jamie went to the kitchen one night to get a drink and there, in the flickering light of the popping gas mantle, was the man. With his grey felt hat on the floor beside him. Balancing a cup of tea and a piece of raisin cake on his knee.

'This is Mr Ecklund', Pearl said.

'How do you do', Jamie said. Formally. And shook hands.

'Midnight again?' Pearl said.

Jamie nodded. Knowing she was flustered.

'All them books', she said. 'Rot yer brain.'

178

Jamie patted her shoulder and went back to his room.

Mr Ecklund became a regular visitor. Stiff on a kitchen chair. Never far separated from his hat. Two and three times a week. And on Pearl's free Sunday they went off together in his trap.

Grandmother did not comment at first, though Jamie knew it would not take her long to solve the mystery. She knew everyone. The town was like Pear's cyclopedia under her hat. Then one day, when 'the man' was mentioned at dinner, after Pearl had taken out the plates, she sniffed.

'A widower . . . with a grown-up brood. It's disgusting.' But she smiled. Slyly. So that Jamie knew she did not mean what she had said.

'Time she was bedded, I daresay. The poor soul's twenty years overdue.'

Pearl didn't alter much. A little softer. The change between one fabric and another. Though when Jamie bought her a lace handkerchief for her birthday she kissed him almost fiercely and said, 'Now clear out of my kitchen.' She had never looked like that before.

The next washing day – Mr Ecklund never appeared on washing nights – when Pearl had washed and dried up and was finishing the ironing, the kitchen stank of scorched sheets. This was so unusual that Jamie decided carelessness must be one of the signs of falling in love. He watched as Pearl slammed the iron back on the range, picked up a hot one and spat on it. The spittle scattered like sandcrabs.

'That Mary is took bad', she said. Watching him.

'What?' Jamie almost shouted.

'Her insides. Operation.'

'How do you know . . . when did you hear?'

'A bird told me.'

Grandmother confirmed. She too had only just heard. She was waiting for more information before she told him. Mary had an abscess on the lung and might not live. He felt sick. He wanted to see her. To be near her. He had never felt so cold and helpless. He went to the private hospital the next afternoon after school but the Matron would not let him see her. He was leaving when Mary's mother came into the reception hall and smiled wanly at him.

'How nice of you', she said. 'They will only let me see her for a moment. I'm sorry.'

'Has she been operated on yet?'

She shook her head. 'If she can survive' . . . her voice faltered – 'we must take her to a specialist.'

'She's strong', he heard himself say.

An empty sound. Like a shout far off inside a scrub.

Every afternoon he rode his bicycle up and down outside the hospital. Frightened for her. Hoping. Wanting to share this awful thing. A wordless pilgrimage. He could not study and once the words of a textbook blurred with tears. He slept fitfully, waking, thinking of her face, hearing over and over again the haunting music from the Show.

Then one night his grandmother came into his room and put a hand on his shoulder.

'There's an improvement. They hope to take her south in a few days. Mary's mother told me you had called and had been to the hospital every day. Mary actually smiled when she heard. Her mother thinks you helped and is very grateful.'

It all sounded meaningless. He had done nothing except wait and hope. The helpless moments. Life was littered with them. Like broken shells on a beach.

He went to the station when Mary left. In a reserved compartment on the Night Mail. He stood at the carriage window. She looked so small and frail he nearly cried out. She lifted her right thumb, the sign they had always used. He returned the signal. The guard blew his whistle and she was gone.

Equilibrium gradually returned. Like a headache fading.

Jamie felt he had been living upside down. Drifting with a tide that had nothing to do with the sea or the river. More a tide moving among the clouds. The pain ebbed and a trembling calm replaced the tension. Then one day his first real suffering was no longer there. More a memory. No longer a reality. The operation was a success. A letter came to Grandmother. But Mary would spend months in hospital. With tubes in her side. Far away. And a long convalescence.

He was relieved and glad and thought of her often. Her lovely face and yellow hair. The colourless face on the colourless pillow. The train pulling out until it was a red spot retreating in the dark. Thought of her more and more distantly, so that across the weeks she became someone he had known in another age when he was another person. Before those days of anguish when he had almost grown up.

CHAPTER SIXTEEN

AT THE END of the period, the last of the day, Miss Pringle said, 'I want to talk to you.'

And Jamie knew.

The form room emptied as she put her books away. She sat at the next desk.

'There's no need for me to tell you that your work lately has been terrible.'

'I know.' And added, after a pause. 'I can't concentrate.'

He wasn't going to tell her why.

'You won't get through unless you do. What's the matter?'

He evaded again. 'Nothing seems to stick.'

'So I've noticed.'

The words were ash. She tapped the desk. The teacher and the pupil. The gulf unbridgeable. To Jamie the meeting at the Show had never happened.

'Now listen to me', she said. 'You have a natural aptitude. One of the few who has. If you're prepared to help yourself I'm prepared to give you some coaching.'

'That's very nice', he began, but she stopped him.

'It's nothing of the kind. I hate to see a good brain going to waste.'

Her voice softened. 'Would you like me to help you?'

'Yes', he said. There was little else he could say.

'Very well. We'll start tomorrow after school. But not here. If I start coaching at school I'll have to coach a dozen. I'm not such a public benefactor as all that. You know where I live – the white house on the corner. I'll be there by half past four.'

Miss Pringle had just made tea when Jamie arrived. She carried the pot to her room at the back of the house.

'My landlady's in Brisbane for six months. We won't be interrupted.' And added, a little grimly Jamie thought, 'I hope this doesn't take as long as all that.'

The room, an addition into the back garden, was large, divided in two. A bed, under a white counterpane, with a white mosquito net suspended from a ring and tucked in at the back, shared one end with a dressing table. The other half, separated by a Chinese bamboo screen, contained two easy chairs, a desk and a bookcase.

They pulled the chairs together and drank their tea as they started work.

She was a good teacher. Even better than before a class. She persuaded rather than taught. Discussed the work so that the puzzle pieces fitted together. She worked with an impatient enthusiasm that was so infectious that after only a few days he was learning quickly and enjoying it.

Miss Pringle had a curious habit of bending towards him, closing one eye and saying, 'Say it aloud. This is a sweet language. Say it and you'll remember it. Don't worry about the accent. It will come.'

Her teeth were irregular but very white. She had a tiny mole on each earlobe. He had never noticed them before. She had a pleasant smell.

At the end of the first week she snapped the grammar and smiled.

'*Vous avez fait des progrès, M'sieur.*'

Then she yawned, stretched her arms above her head until an elbow cracked like a dry stick and patted her back hair. A pin fell out and then another. The hair loosened and fell down her back, almost to her waist. Like an idea unfolding.

183

'Clumsy', she said.

Jamie, standing now and about to go, watched it fall and wanted to touch it. To feel its texture, to stroke it. He went behind her and slid a wide strand through his fingers. He could not stop himself. She looked up and back at him, the way a child will, reached back quickly and touched his arm. Just for a moment. Then she swung forward and was on her feet, looking at him with the same measuring expression he had first seen in the softdrink tent.

'I think it's time you went home', she said.

Jamie was bemused. Had he made himself ridiculous? Had he been presumptuous, insulting? He tried to think of words that fitted. But they only created more words and more muddle in his mind. She had not screamed or slapped him or appeared insulted. She had even reached back and touched him.

At home he grinned back from the mirror. Would she report him to the Head or refuse to coach him or ignore the incident? Then a niggling suspicion began to form. A suspicion that became a near-certainty. She would do none of these things. She liked him touching her hair.

On the Monday she was friendly but businesslike. Even a little more brusque than usual. Or perhaps that was imagination. She did not refer to what had happened. But he was no longer sure. Certainty faded. They worked hard for an hour. He tried to concentrate but he was conscious of her nearness, her eyes almost turquoise in the subdued light, her dusty smell as she reached closer and corrected a sentence.

'Enough', she said at last. And relaxed in her chair, her arms limp at the sides.

He took the pins out and let down her hair. He found a brush on the dressing table and stroked. She turned sideways, so that the hair fell straight, and closed her eyes.

'Lovely', she said. 'Lovely.'

He bent and kissed her and she held him. But only for a moment. She pushed him away.

'Young man', she said. 'This can't go on.'

Every afternoon Jamie brushed her hair. Holding it and sweeping it from the scalp to the turned up ends. The brush whispered. A dry impossible sound.

'Lovely', she said. And kissed him and kissed him.

Then one Friday she let him in and closed the door quickly and put her arms around him. The blinds were down. She was wearing a kimono of red silk. It was all she wore. She held him and kissed him and unbuttoned his shirt. As she undressed him he felt scared and wild and breathless. He wanted to run and knew he must stay. Wanted to stay and knew he must run. She brought him to the bed and pulled back the sheet and lay between him and her cool hands held him. She showed him and helped him and taught him. And in a rocking pulsing screaming pulsing world they submerged and drowned.

Each afternoon they drowned.

And Jamie's French got worse and worse.

On that first evening, as he hurried home, his mind raced as his pulse had raced at her first touch. His head was full of beetles. Scurrying. He tried to sort his thoughts and feelings, to find answers to the impact of that exploding hour. But the thoughts clashed. Out of control. Specimens in a poison bottle. Kicking, jerking as they died.

Everyone knew. He was sure. And wanted to hide. People looked at him and sniggered. Ridiculous. But intermingled with the other darting signals, the thought persisted. Someone called his name from the footpath but he rode on. Without even the softening gesture of a wave. He felt certain that he must carry a mark, some distinguishing sign, must look so different that people would nudge each other and say, 'That's him.' He knew shame and with it a squirming kind of fright. An icy withdrawal. Shame for what he had done and what it would do to him and to her. To him. To her. To him. The tyres sang the words. What had he done? What had he started? What feathers had been plucked to expose his nakedness? Would he now go slowly inexorably revoltingly blind or mad? As some of the boys said you did.

He locked himself in his room. Glad of the quiet of the empty house, except for Pearl at the other end in her kitchen. He approached the mirror, yet frightened to face it. Edged up to it as if it would strike him, not knowing what he would see but expecting a mark, a sign, some disfigurement he would never be able to cover or hide. A brand he would never keep from Grandmother or Pearl or a sneering world. They stared at each other, two in the silent room. Stared secretly, furtively. Afraid.

Jamie studied his sweaty face. Damp and red from the bicycle ride from her place. The freckles prominent. The whites of his eyes a little streaky. But he had those kind of eyes anyhow. Otherwise unchanged, unmarked, except for a pin-prick of blood on his right ear. He stared until his eyes watered, until he realised he was holding his breath. A long relaxing whoosh of inexpressible relief. He wiped the speck of blood with spit on his handkerchief and let himself down into his easy chair.

The relief was violent. The effects of the opium pills when he developed an abscess in his little finger. The finger, three times its normal size, that the doctor would not lance until it was ripe.

Now, as the tensions ebbed, streaming out of him like the pus and blood from the opened finger, he could think again, and gradually, as though recovering from a state of shock, a whispering pride replaced the early anguish and fright. The great mystery had been solved, and would be solved again.

Mystery, revelation. Creation, meaning, soul. Now he was elated. The music from that day again drifted from the sky and covered him.

He returned to the mirror. Unmarked. Unchanged. As he had been before it happened. He smiled and the boy no longer smiled back. He began to laugh. Quietly and uncontrollably. He laughed so much he was almost sick.

Only later did another reaction come. Crowding in on him. Would others, those who were close, recognise some change in him? Some subtle or obvious sign or gesture or difference that would betray him. Caged, he remained on guard. Stayed in his room as much as possible. Working?

At school it was easier. He felt immeasurably older. And even more apart from his fellows. He laughed at the jokes and the dirty stories. Smiled inwardly at the fumbling ignorance. But some of the more mature girls looked at him with questioning eyes, or he thought they did, as though they responded to some change in him. He felt that girls, even young girls, knew less but understood more than boys of their own age. Or was this his own imagining?

Mostly, Jamie wondered how he would react to Miss Pringle and she to him. He waited. Tight as a buggy rim hammered at the smithy. But he need not have worried. In the classroom she was friendly, natural, as she had been when the coaching afternoons had begun. He received no special attention. Nor did she ignore him, which he thought she might. Once she even sat beside him and corrected a translation. He tried to follow the changes but his mouth was emery paper. He closed his eyes, sweating at the thought of her small high breasts against him.

Only after she moved to another student did Jamie realise, with a jolt, that she, himself, others were two people and perhaps many times more than two people. That behind the faces he saw every day were other faces, hidden, secretive, forlorn, fearful. That people, just ordinary people, had many lives hidden from view, washed by the waves and currents of hate and love and imagination and what was and what might have been and what could never be.

Every afternoon he, a different person, lay with that other Miss Pringle, her long hair seaweed in shallow water. He could not do without her. That other person. She was need, demand, idea. A fantasy. Urgent. An irresistible need he had never suspected. Every time he died and was renewed and died again. A snake shedding its skin. Beyond that he could not know or feel. Beyond was unimaginable. If this was love he needed no other explanation, no excuse, no alchemy. It was enough. And enough that had no end and no beginning and was never started and never fulfilled.

Every Sunday Jamie waited for Monday. Chained to weighted hours. His aimlessness almost a sickness. He could not work. He went for long walks and returned to words that could have been Chinese. But one Sunday he glanced into the drawing room, at his grandmother in her rocking chair. And thought she was asleep and moved down the hall towards his room.

'Boy', she called. 'Come here this instant.'

She called him that only if she had something important to say. Or worse, was displeased. He sat beside her. Her parchment hands rested on knees so sharp they seemed to split her dress. Her eyes were points of light in a frayed curtain. South American shrunken heads he had seen in *The Illustrated London News* at the School of Arts.

'Who is she?'

The question slapped. She knew. But how.

'Who is who?' he parried. Trying to sound casual, to hold the shakes inside him.

'Don't play games with me, boy.'

The words spears.

He told her. He had always told her. He kept nothing back. It had always been part of their oneness. The name. How it had begun. When and where. Telling was easier than he thought it would be. He felt better. Weightless at last. Free. But still astonished that the impossible had happened.

She grunted. 'How old is she?'

'Twenty-three.'

'Good. The woman should be older – the first time.'

She peered at him. 'It is the first?'

'Yes.'

'I knew. I just thought I'd ask.'

She closed her eyes and rocked. Jamie watched her. Bewildered by her perception, at what she had said. He felt puppy young. Innocent beside her. A child. Alarmed at his own blundering innocence and ignorance. Yet grateful for her acceptance. For the lack of preaching. Though she rarely preached.

'How did you know?'

He had to ask. Had wanted to ask the moment he knew she knew.

'It's not the first time I've seen rut', she said, opening her eyes. 'It's spread all over you. Thick as strawberry jam.'

Now he felt helpless. Thinking of that first afternoon when he looked for a mark, some disgusting sign of guilt.

'How does it show?'

'Show, you young fool. It doesn't show. It's not something I see but something I know. A tomcat has it after his first pounce.'

Grandmother stilled the rocker.

'Is she clean?'

Jamie wasn't sure what she meant. He had heard of diseases but could not imagine Miss Pringle having anything like that.

'Very clean. She smells of lemon peel.'

'By the great Lord Harry.' She almost choked. Her body rattled with a dry wheezing laugh. 'Lemon peel'. Her eyes filled. The laughter tears spread down her lined cheeks. She wiped them with a cambric handkerchief she kept up her long sleeve.

'Now listen to me', she managed to say at last. 'It had to happen some time. I'm glad you mafficked with this Miss . . . . What's her name?'

'Pringle!'

'Doesn't she have another?'

'Jane.'

'"Then let Jane Shaw with sorrow sing.

That was beloved of a king."'

'What?'

'Nothing. An echo.'

Her faded eyes came back to the room. To Jamie.

'You heard what I said.'

He hadn't but he listened.

'It won't last. It won't and it can't. Against nature. The girl's years ahead of you. Beyond the tomcat stage. If you realise that you won't get badly hurt. I mean it. I've seen young men go to pieces with the first woman hurt – and stay in pieces. But women – never. Women are not made of sugar and spice and everything nice. They come from earth and rock. They're made to survive.'

She closed her eyes and rested her head against the back. He waited. Wondering if she had gone to sleep.

'What are you waiting for?' she demanded. 'Clear out. I've almost missed my nap.'

He put his arms around her frail shoulders. 'You're the most wonderful Gran I'll ever know.'

'Tosh', she said. 'I'm a crumbling old hag with one foot in

the grave and the other on a pawpaw skin. They're more slippery than bananas. Now out with you.'

As he reached the door he heard her repeat, just loud enough for him to hear, 'Lemon peel. Lemon peel.'

The day after full moon was a Saturday. They left with the sunrise and drove in the borrowed dogcart along the south road before turning towards the sea. The town still slept but the cane cutters were moving. In heavy boots and battered hats with their lunches in carrying bags slung on their backs or tied to the handlebars. They were clean and shaved, but in the afternoon would ride back to town, dog weary, stinging from cane slashes, black as kanakas from the burnt trash. All except their eyes.

They saw the sea glitter from near the Mount down a mile-long avenue of waving cane topped with violet feather duster flowers and took another track south between the low walls of morticed stone the kanakas had built with craftmen's hands fifty years before as they planted the first cane.

'Where are we going?' she asked.

'Sandhills Beach.'

'Lovely. Miles from nowhere.'

'That's why I picked it.'

She held his hand and smiled into him. She was almost beautiful that hot and cloudless morning under her yellow hat, clamped with a white scarf tied under her chin, and her white dotted blue cotton dress. They laughed and sang and didn't care how slowly the mare trotted the five miles to the beach.

'I shall always remember this morning', she said.

'There will be plenty more.'

She pointed suddenly, changing the subject, to the long low stone wall that held two fields apart.

'Like something you would see in England or France.'

Sandhills Beach was a crescent of butter-coloured sand between brooding basalt headlands, and beyond the points the sea broke gently on splayed reefs. Behind the beach the sandhills climbed steeply and on their sides and crests perched breadfruit trees whose parchment leaves clashed in the breeze, and on the slopes sand-vines trailed their thick saucer leaves and pale blue bell-like flowers. Beyond again, where they left the dogcart and hobbled the horse, was a grove of she-oaks.

They slid down the hills, starting little avalanches, and on the beach took off their clothes and hand in hand went into the sea among the darting whiting in the shallows. They swam and played and climbed on the volcano's ancient rocks against a sea now deep blue close in and citron far out where the swell began. They came back to a beach moving with millions of scarlet and blue sand-crabs. Parading battalions, the Grand Army at Austerlitz, but never mixing, never engaging, always marching in drilled formations with a clicking scrabbling step towards the water to dig themselves in and disappear.

They searched for ugaries with their toes and found a star shell and a Chinaman's hat and a reddish brown shark's egg, a shattered pomegranate, with a split in its leathery covering through which a sharkling had been born.

Dry now, with salt smears on their bodies, they climbed the sandhills and entered the she-oaks where the fallen needles lay deep and quiet. And there they joined and slept and ate and slept and loved again.

After the last time she clung to him with a new and desperate fierceness and said, again and again, 'I never want this day to end.' She pressed her face against his shoulder and began to cry. He tried to comfort her but knew the foolishness of words.

Later, from the top of the sandhills, they said goodbye to the kindly beach and the last of that golden day. A thin sea mist crept in between the headlands. Straggling sea birds were going home, far out and close to the pewter sea. The moment passed and they turned away.

It was almost dark when Jamie harnessed the mare and they began the journey back through the fields. A hushed journey as though the day itself was spent. She sat with her arm through his as the wheels of the dogcart jolted in the ruts. They did not speak. There was nothing to say.

They drove between cane fires under their sky glow. The burning was all around them, cauldrons of fire as the farmers made ready for the next day. The crackling cane threw handfuls of sparks into the night and the debris from burnt trash drifted across them. The air was brown and weighted with the smell of burning. The ash across them was a dark drifting rain.

Jamie did not see her the next day. It wasn't possible. And on Monday a new French teacher was in charge of the form.

He read the letter. Racing along the words. He went to the dunny and sat on the seat lid and cried. She had been transferred. She couldn't tell him. She had tried. How hard she had tried! The words would not come. Perhaps it was better this way. He was the sweetest person she had ever known. She would never forget. . . .

Jamie was angry, bitter. Her desertion close to hate. The longing for her was a new and impossible sickness. He poured it all into one tormented letter. He never received a reply.

CHAPTER SEVENTEEN

JAMIE found only one antidote. He began to work with a frenzy that astonished him. At night he drove himself, sleeping only a few hours, and at daylight rising to work again.

She returned again and again but he tried to ignore her, not to think of her. When she was close he pushed her face away, back into the dark. The bile in his throat, sour and burning. His thoughts flashes of light, shattered sentences, torn pictures with burnt edges. Love and hate so close he could not hold them apart.

Then one night he stopped work as the post office clock slow beat an intolerable midnight, and in the silence, alive with ghosts after the last note, she was back again. Inside his head. Behind his eyes. The cool voice, her slow laugh. He tried to drive her out but she would not go. Words emerged. Her words. But he could not hear them. And then, clearer, something about faith. He sat listening to her, to the caves deep within himself. He who loses integrity. He tossed the words away and in their place were others. Not he who loses integrity. He who loses faith in his own integrity knows disgust. Something like that. The voice from behind his eyes. Quotation without a source. She had said it once, and there was more, after they had loved, in the total rest of communion, the dim and impossible peace in the lateness of a folding day. Now the words had returned and she was still there, still part of him, separate but still part, as she had been on that first day. And he knew that he was grateful.

Above Boola Street the clock beat one, and she was gone. Never to return except in fragments of memory, when pain had disappeared and even regret had faded like the last splashes of gold and crimson above the hills of the cattle country.

And then the exams were above the horizon, swirling towards him, sweeping all debris aside until on the final day, when the last papers were pinned, he knew he was through. Not by much, but through. Instinct told him. Or was it certainty through her, from her, because of her?

He rode back to the big house late that afternoon, with the swans heading for the swamps beyond Saxony. Not glad or elated but heavy and beaten. A compelling weariness that spread upwards through his body. And when it reached his head he fainted.

For the first time ever Grandmother fussed. And Pearl was more convinced than ever that all them books had rotted his brain. But the doctor found nothing wrong with him that sleep would not mend. He went to bed for two days and sat under the mango tree and listened to the silence and was well again. He returned to school, not to work but to rehearse. As Hamlet. He could not act but none of the others suited the part. And his was the only voice that would carry with any conviction to the back row of the Assembly Hall.

Days later they were still rehearsing, now in costume to get the movements right, still striving to make the words come from living people. The English master despaired. No talent existed among them and they knew it. They laboured like draught horses, drawing the beautiful lines behind them like heavy carts.

Then the world stopped. For a moment. And began to spin again.

Jamie had just finished a scene when the headmaster rushed in shouting, 'The war's over. The war's over.' And put his handkerchief to his eyes and wept.

They surrounded him. Sprayed him with questions.

'The news has just come through', he said. 'They rang me from the telegraph office. The carnage is over.'

The false armistice that swept the world. The real armistice was still days away. But nobody knew or would have cared. The war was over.

Jamie and the cast gathered the school drums and the bugles. Emptied the Head's cupboard of its flags and the blue banners on sticks with the faces of King George and Queen Mary with the royal arms above them. With the school behind them they marched, under grey overcast in a gusting wind, round and round the football field, led by Hamlet and Horatio and Ophelia, and the headmaster with a Union Jack draped about his shoulders. They shouted and belted the kettledrums and made the bugles speak and sang *Land of Hope and Glory* and *Rule Britannia* and *Boys of the Bulldog Breed* and *Pack Up Your Troubles* and *Tipperary* and *Three Cheers for The Red White and Blue* until they were hoarse. And then, massed before the main steps, they raised every flag they had on the school pole and sang, again and again between the cheering, *God Save the King.*

As Jamie rode home the town was wild. Flowers and torn paper and streamers and flags. He had never suspected before there were so many flags in the town. The band, in working clothes, was parading up and down playing patriotic songs and from the Royal and Commercial barrels were being rolled and broached. The celebration continued all night and in the morning, which few saw and none clearly, Boola Street was a litter of rubbish and broken glass.

But above on the post office tower, almost unnoticed yet, the red cyclone flag was ironed by the wind against a racing sky and gusts from the sea slammed the town and rattled the windows. Every hour the wind was stronger, whining and moaning through the steets. And then the rain began. Early afternoon was almost dark. An eclipse dark of flying leaves and frantic birds. And with it came a demented wind, screaming like the bunyip as Grandmother said, that rocked houses and sliced off roofs and drove water into the sturdiest homes.

Jamie watched the tall palm in the front garden bend almost to the ground before it snapped with an artillery shot. The wind stripped the lemon tree and fired them against the house, smashing shutters and windows in a bombardment that burst through the screaming of the cyclone wind. Stripped the mango tree and flung its ripening fruit on to the roof and over against buildings hundreds of yards up River Street.

Then the heavy firebell began to stammer with every blast, though its chill calling could be heard only in the brief lulls. But Prince the firehorse heard it, broke from his box where he had been put when the cyclone began, and trotted to the fire waggon, as he had been taught at the sound of the bell, and backed himself below the suspended shafts. The fireman tried to lead him away from the waggon but he would not move. Stood there, his head away from the wind, waiting like a soldier for orders. The fireman had to climb the swaying bell-tower and lash the clapper before Prince would go back to his stall.

The cyclone lasted for two days. Two days and twenty inches of rain. A brown flood swept down from the hills and the river jumped its banks. Then as the rain eased and the wind retreated to the sea, farmers for miles around cursed as they got to their cane. Driven flat on the red fields or washed into tangles in the chocolate gullies. And in town people emerged as the overcast broke into scuds to start replacing roofs and clearing streets and gardens of sheets of iron and timber and uprooted trees. The sun returned at last like a frightened child. The wind joined others in the Coral Sea. The town steamed.

Jamie went back to school and to *Hamlet*. But not for long.

'That Mrs Scully', Pearl said, bringing in the vegetables. ''Eard she kicked th' bucket.'

'It's only too true', Grandmother said. 'Poor soul.'

'She wasn't very old', Jamie said. 'Was it this influenza?'

Grandmother nodded. 'Doctor thinks the germ is already here. Carried back by the soldiers. He's very worried.'

Within days of Mrs Scully's funeral three people had it and two days later another two. People called it the influenza or the pneumonic or just the diease. The word pandemic, which Jamie looked up in the dictionary, began to be heard. At school boys and girls brought alarming rumours from their homes. You went black or choked. Or your insides came out. Some said that more young people than grownups got it. Then, as the disease spread, and the holidays were near, the schools were closed. There never was a *Hamlet*.

He came home to a meeting in the drawing room. His grandmother and others had organised a nursing service to help people in their homes. The two hospitals were crowded. The public with mattresses in the corridors. The doctor was run off his feet. All over town, in every house in some streets, someone had the influenza or the pneumonic.

Grandmother's committee divided the work and Jamie helped. One woman organised the making of masks from bent wire and lint. They reminded Jamie of chloroform masks. He shuddered when he put his on but the doctor said they might be some protection from the germs. Another woman gathered cooking pots and containers. Others collected baskets or money or food or medical supplies or provided buggies or buckboards.

The kitchen range at the big house was never cold as Pearl

and two helpers cut meat and vegetables and chopped bones or made custards and jellies. Mutton broth simmered in the biggest saucepans. The heat from the almost permanent fire soaked into the house so that Jamie felt he was living in a culture flask. The house stank of cooking. Even the sheets and pillows. Even his handkerchiefs.

Each morning Jamie collected a list of urgent cases from the doctor. The baker's wife with nobody to look after the five children. Or the old widow who lived by the creek who had been ill and on her own for two days. Or a whole family in Chinatown. The Chows seemed to get it worse than white families.

Each morning Grandmother and Jamie put on their masks, which almost covered their faces and were suffocating in the summer heat, and set off in the Ford. Jamie did not have a permit to drive but in the emergency the new Sergeant looked the other way. Grandmother would do what she could to clean people and make them comfortable, or solve some problem over children or supplies, or even take down the details of a death if one had not been reported. She would tell Jamie what food was needed and he would then drive home, collect the containers of soup and jelly and other things from Pearl and return. This continued every day. Late at night they went to bed, exhausted, and tried to forget the horrors they had seen.

Jamie first detected the peculiar smell in every house where the influenza had struck. Wet mice but slightly saccharine. Unmistakable. He quickly recognised the signs of the travelling sickness. The short harsh cough at the beginning which soon softened and almost disappeared. The flushed face and quickened breathing. The complaint of chest pains. But worse, so that at first he shivered when he saw it, the heliotrope of almost certain death. Deep purple blotches on the face, early, though later the lethal colour spread down to the

chest. Most of these were pneumonia cases, rattling and choking in delirium. They died, many of them, within a day or so
of the first headache, the first mild rigors.

Jamie also noticed how the influenza was impartial and
irrational. It struck every family in one street and ignored
and continued to ignore another. Or one person in a family
got it and the others escaped. For some patients, whose
influenza never turned to pneumonia, it meant only a week
in bed and slow unsteady convalescence. For others, pneumonia, the heliotrope blotches and quick death in coma. Some
people had only a mild attack and developed the dreaded
pneumonia later, even when they were almost well. Others
started with pneumonia and died quickly not marked with
purple but with jaundice. The colour of blood oranges, their
lips encrusted with the scabs of herpes, all muscular control
gone. They lay unconscious, jerking in their own filth.

To Jamie they were stinking, frightening days and nights,
yet suffering and death was so commonplace, so much a
reality of staying alive, that he became accustomed to it. He
was astonished at first that he could watch, emotionless, a
dying patient. Even ashamed. But astonishment and shame
did not last. He saw too much of the sickness. Day after day.
He was too tired. But he never mastered the helpless feeling
the sickness brought him and Grandmother and others who
fought it. The influenza was an enemy but they could not
even treat its symptoms. No medicine ever helped. Nothing
would stop it. Even the Chinese admitted that their remedies
were useless. Every day he watched old and young dying and
knew that one of the earliest rumours was true. More young
people seemed to die. More often the youngest and strongest
first.

In one house Jamie and his grandmother visited, Horatio
from *Hamlet*, deep purple on his face and shoulders. And only
minutes dead. He rushed into the backyard and was sick. In

another house they found Old Mick, sitting on the side of his bed, spitting and growling between his coughing, 'I'm buggered if I'm going to die.'

It was Old Mick who reminded Jamie. He had not seen the Professor for days. He had not given him a thought. But at the first lull he drove out to his shanty on the edge of town, and even as he left the car he knew with hopeless certainty that he was too late.

The Professor, his head pillowed on his coat, stared up at Jamie. His skin was marked with the fading heliotrope and the stain spread down his neck. Beside him were two empty bottles of brandy. And weighted with one bottle was a sheet of paper. With 'For Jamie' at the top.

He sat on the sugarbag mat and studied the almost copperplate writing and wondered how such a dirty unkempt man could write so beautifully.

'A long time ago', the letter began, 'you did me the honour, dear boy, of reliving the Boorool with me and I'm sure understanding the significance and beauty of that ancient ceremony. I meant to repay you. I never did. I shall do it now before it is too late. Death is coming soon. There will be no grim reaper. It will be like birth and as natural as the birds.

'If you will study the left-hand post of your back gate you will distinguish certain curious marks. You have probably never noticed them before. There are two short parallel lines cut into the paint. There is a minute crescent, a square that would fit a threepenny piece without touching the rim, and others. Those marks, hard to distinguish unless you know what to look for, were made by wandering tramps and ne'er-do-wells, the fraternity of the road, the gentlemen of the open sky, swaggies with billies, men like myself. They left them there for the instruction and the benefit of others, to inform them that the house within those gates was a house of compassion and charity. Those marks on the post could be described as the swagman's own newspaper. They mean that in the home within is shelter, food, medicines and bandages and that these things will be given freely, without question, without preaching and with love. There is one mark, however, a cross, which is a warning to all of the wandering fraternity never to expect too much from life. The cross means that he who would beg money in this house, and money to the fraternity means alcohol, will assuredly be sent away with a flea in his ear. Food, shelter and succour. Yes. A temple of charity in an un-Christian world. And the giver of that charity, freely and without obligation, is someone who is dear to us both, your grandmother. She is, without the shadow of a doubt, the one and only memorable woman of my misspent life. I love her for what she is and what she has been to me. My truest friend. I love her for what she is to you and to so many others in this township. I know, dear boy, that at this very moment she is killing herself in the service of the needy. As she took me in once and nursed me, a dirty stranger, back to health. I would like to remind you that there are only two majestic words in the English language, and those are love and compassion. I do not preach. That is for lesser men. But unless you know what love and compassion mean and what they imply in the relationships of human kind, you will never know what life is all about.

'And now, dear boy, I give to you the only thing I have to leave after a life of useless indulgence which I have enjoyed to the full. It is the last remnant of a once great private collection. It is precious to me for some illogical reason. I hope that it remains precious to you. Make sure you get it when I am with my dark friends of the dreamtime.'

Jamie put down the paper and saw the dillybag in the dead hands. The ancient Aboriginal dillybag the Professor had once shown him. Made by gins long dead from possum skin and human hair and embroidered in coloured seeds. He dragged it gently from the dead fingers. They did not want to let it go. He picked up the letter and left the shanty. He did not cry. The Professor would have approved.

Jamie gave Grandmother the bag and the letter. She read it through, stared unblinking at the far wall, and read it again.

'The old reprobate', she said. 'Too proud to come here again. I would have nursed him.'

The hand on the dillybag in her lap trembled. Enough to make the silver possum fur shimmer.

He saw now, more than ever before, how tired she was. How much she had aged in the last awful weeks. Her eyes had sunk deeper into her face. Almost out of sight. Like Nosey's.

She handed back the letter and the bag. 'Keep them – always.'

He put a hand on her shoulder, against the bones.

'You must rest', he said. Gently. ·

'Tosh', she said. 'How can one rest?'

CHAPTER EIGHTEEN

When the epidemic was beginning, Hans Schultz still had time and energy to pay the last courtesies. He still drove the hearse to the cemetery. And if the coffin held a child he replaced the black drapes over his horses with white net and the black plumes on their collars with white plumes.

But as the sickness worsened he was forced to abandon conventional funerals. His stock of French-polished coffins was soon used and, with no carpenter to renew his supply, he searched the districts for wood and scrounged in Chinatown and on the wharves for tea chests and fruit boxes and even cardboard that could be pasted together with flour and water and stained with varnish.

For two days each week he worked at the cemetery digging a common grave. There were no men to help him. And on the third he borrowed a German waggon from one of the farms, loaded it with his crude coffins and creaked along Cemetery Road at night and filled in part of the mass grave, helped by the priest, the parson or the relatives, and returned to town with the empties.

Jamie saw him one night in upper Boola Street. Asleep on the front of the waggon, with a smoking hurricane lantern beside him, the reins limp in his folded hands, the black horses just moving the waggon. He didn't wake him. The horses knew the way back to the funeral parlor.

Jamie wondered how long these days could continue. At the hospitals the nurses were getting an hour's sleep when they could. In their uniforms. On the floor. The doctor had not slept for three days. All the volunteer helpers were exhausted. And some were ill. Two with the pneumonic. He wondered how long his grandmother could withstand the cruel pressure. She would work all day and go out at night because she felt her presence was needed or that she might by some miracle save a life. He watched her on one of these nights, with love and admiration, leaning over a bed, her forehead twisted and shrunken with weariness above the white mask, the little strength she had going out to the sick woman with the heliotrope blotches already on her face.

'We must make her rest more', he said to Pearl, when they returned.

'Try'n git yer granny t'do somethin' she don't want. Some women's made that way.'

And then one morning, just before breakfast, after being out until after midnight, Grandmother called Jamie to her bedroom.

'Get the list from the doctor and do what you can. I'm tired. Wake me up at five o'clock . . . and not a minute later.'

She slept all day. When he went to her room she was sitting up. Undoing one of her rat-tail plaits.

'I feel a new woman', she said. 'Almost.'

She had a hot bath, put on her best black dress and even pinned a black velvet ribbon in her hair. At the back. And another ribbon round her net collar. She came in to supper, smiling. As Jamie held her chair he saw she was wearing all her rings.

'You look . . . beautiful', Jamie said.

'Thank you', she said, and held up both hands. 'They will add a little light to a dark world.' And added, 'I think he would have approved.'

Jamie knew who she meant.

She was strangely gay and talkative that evening. Younger,

too. In a subtle way he could not explain. The great weariness seemed to have left her. And after the meal she sat in her rocking chair and talked about her childhood.

And his own childhood raced back to him.

Jamie had heard the stories many times. They were part of him and of her. Strands in the web that bound them. Yet this night they sounded different. Almost at times as if he were hearing them for the first time. Perhaps he understood them more. Understood her more. Was closer to her. If that was possible.

She told again how she had learnt to swim. One of his favourites. How the gins had crept up from the camp below the homestead and had taken his grandmother and her sister and swum with them on their backs into the middle of the Murrumbidgee. How they had taught them to paddle, to swim native fashion, to dive like water birds. And she only three and her sister only five and their terrified mother screaming on the bank.

She told of the night of the yellow flood when the river was three times its size and boiling with trees and fencing rails and drowned sheep. When the rain drummed the slabs of the lonely homestead just above the flood and inside two flickering candles in pewter sticks stood on the red tasselled cloth covering the mahogany table that had come out in the black and gold Indiaman. And around the table was her mother and the four children.

Jamie knew the story by heart. Every word and incident. But this night he was in the room itself. The room his Grandmother had known as a child.

'"There's a horse coming", John said. John was my eldest brother. He was eleven and big, with freckles and sandy hair. A little like you, Jamie.' Her voice was faint but clear.

'"It's the rain", Mother said.

'"A horse just crossed the flint patch. Father never uses that track."

'We waited. Straining. Counting the drips in the leather bucket from the leak in the kitchen.

'"Someone outside", John said. And lifted a candle.

'"Who could it be . . . on a night like this?" Mother said.

'John went to the door. Shading the candle. As his eyes adjusted to the dark he saw a black horseman against the night. Through the silver rain.

'The stranger dismounted and came to the door. Water dripped from his beard and from the rim of his cabbage-tree hat. He was tall and young.

'"Is there a bridge? I must get across."

'"No", John said. "And the crossing's covered."

'He didn't like the accent or the man. Something about him. The hour. The flood.

'"We can't help you", Mother said. From behind her guttering candle.

'"Have you a boat?" the stranger asked.

'"No", John said. Too quickly. Thinking of it pulled up the slope above where the black's camp had been.

'"A boat wouldn't help you in this flood", Mother reminded him. And she added, being a kindly woman, "You're very wet. You're welcome to the barn."

'"Thank you, Missus. But I must get across somewhere."

'As he turned abruptly his rain heavy coat swung aside and they saw the black holster. They heard him ride away.

'"Bolt the door", Mother said.

'"Did you see the pistol?"

'She nodded. Grimly. "No God fearing man wears one in these parts."

"Do you think . . . ?"

"The man who bailed up the store over the mountains. They said he was young – and a Paddy."

'By daylight the rain was easing. The boat was gone. But we had to wait for Father's return for the rest of the story. The bushranger had crossed the flood with the horse behind the boat. He had stolen a fresh horse further south and crossed into Victoria. Outside a store a boy had seen the pistol as he dismounted. He had called to his father, the local trooper, who was inside. The bushranger shot the boy and was killed by the father as he was galloping away.'

Grandmother rocked gently, backwards and forwards, until Jamie felt she must be tired of story telling. He could still hear the rain on the slabs of her childhood a thousand miles, centuries away, still smell the whale grease of the candles, still hear the logs growling as they reached the bend, still see the black horseman against the rain.

She began again. But now she talked of things he had never heard before. She spoke of her father, his great-grandfather. At first he could not follow what she was saying. Then some of the words emerged.

'Drunk again. Yes. Again. He rode off with that whore across his saddle and Mother cried. She cried until she had no more tears. But she took him back. She always took him back. He was a wicked man.'

She closed her eyes and smiled. And then a thin dribble of words and twisted sentences. So low they were almost inaudible. Something about an orchard. Blossoms and the smell of cold apples. And among the aimless sounds that followed the word snow quite distinctly. Once after that he thought she mentioned a name, but he couldn't be sure.

Jamie waited but that was all. The rocker had stopped. She seemed to be asleep. Breathing softly as a kitten. He hesitated before creeping out to the kitchen.

'Leave 'er be', Pearl said. 'I'll git somethin' fer 'er shoulders.'

Jamie went back and Pearl followed with a shawl. But first

she turned down the gas mantle so that the light would not shine in Grandmother's eyes.

'She hasn't moved', he said.

Pearl went to put the shawl around her shoulders but stopped. Frowning. She touched the wrinkled forehead. Touched her on the shoulder and felt her hands. She looked at Jamie.

'She's gone.'

CHAPTER NINETEEN

ON HIS LAST evening Jamie climbed the mango tree, barren of fruit since the cyclone, still almost barren of leaves. He stared upriver to where the sea-eagles nested and on to the hills. His eyes climbed down again from the copper outcrops and the lamplighter was coming along River Street and behind him was the pieman.

Tomorrow was another Christmas Eve, but tomorrow was the past. He would not see it or join the men at first light with his axe or watch the German waggons coming into town. Did not want to see it. He would be going away from the river and the black scrubs. South where the birds had headed at the beginning of all the indolent summers of his life.

He had only one regret. Leaving her. Deserting her. The thought persisted. Like the memory of pain on a still night.

She was beside the Professor. Just across the church line and in sight of Scanlon's headstone the Council had paid for. At least they were together. And his past was them both.

He climbed down and went to the bird house and opened the wire door. It was still light but the parrots were sleepy. He wiped them off their perches. Towards the door. Towards their freedom. They took off, screeching. Circled once and returned to settle in the mango tree. Leaves of crimson and blue against the approaching night. Twigs of emerald. At daylight they would fly.

In the early hours Old Mick brought the cab around. He had insisted, although still shaky from the sickness. Pearl carried out one of the bags and they drove to the station together. But she would not stay. Beside the cab she held him. Held him so he felt she would never let him go. Then she got back into the cab.

A few friends saw him off. There were not many left. He was glad when the night mail clashed at the couplings and began to move.

Soon they were through the scrub and past the show-grounds and into the Hungry Country. At the Two Mile the engine blew its whistle. High lonely and sad. Going away. Going south. Going south. . . .

Only then did the tears come.